The
Reading
Of Poetry

1966

ALLYN and BACON, Inc.

Boston • Rockleigh, N.J. • Atlanta • Dallas • Belmont, Calif.

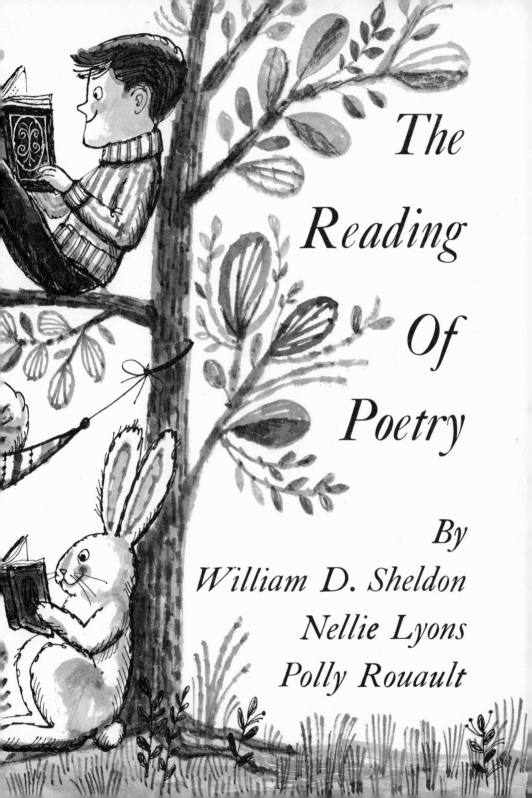

The Reading Of Poetry

By
William D. Sheldon
Nellie Lyons
Polly Rouault

Artwork By

DON MADDEN

Acknowledgments

Grateful acknowledgment is made to authors, publishers, and others for their permission to include the following poems:

Abelard-Schuman Limited for "All Dressed Up for Easter," "Autumn Rain," "Hayfield," "Just a Mile Beyond," "Pussy-Willows," "Taking Down the Tree," and "Wind" from *Runny Days, Sunny Days* by Aileen Fisher, copyright, 1958. Reprinted by permission of the publishers.

Louise Andrews for "I Wish That My Room Had a Floor" from *The Burgess Nonsense Book* by Gelett Burgess.

Appleton-Century-Crofts, Inc. for "A Rainy Day" and "November's Come" from *Cape Cod Ballads* by Joseph C. Lincoln, copyright, 1910, D. Appleton and Company; "The Flower-Fed Buffaloes" from *Going to the Stars* by Vachel Lindsay, copyright, 1962, D. Appleton and Company; "A Ballad of China" from *I Have a Song to Sing You* by Laura E. Richards, copyright, 1938, D. Appleton-Century Company, Inc. Reprinted by permission of the publishers Appleton-Century-Crofts, Inc.

Rowena Bennett for "The Witch of Willowby Wood."

Brandt and Brandt for "Thomas Jefferson," "Christopher Columbus," "Lewis and Clark," and "Clipper Ships and Captains" by Stephen Vincent Benét, and "Nancy Hanks" by Rosemary Carr Benét from *A Book of Americans* by Rosemary and Stephen Vincent Benét, copyright, 1933, by Rosemary and Stephen Vincent Benét, copyright renewed, 1961, by Rosemary Carr Benét; "Everyone Sang" from *Picture Show* by Siegfried Sassoon, copyright, 1920, by E. P. Dutton and Company, Inc.; "Bung Yer Eye" by Stewart Edward White, copyright, 1902, 1930, by Stewart Edward White. Reprinted by permission.

Carol R. Brink for "Goody O'Grumpity."

Bruce Humphries, Inc. for "Wild Geese" from *The City and Other Poems* by Elinor Chipp.

Jonathan Cape Ltd. and Mrs. H. M. Davies for "The Elements" and "Leisure" by W. H. Davies from *The Collected Poems of W. H. Davies.*

Carl Carmer for "Antique Shop."

Joseph Cherwinski for "A Still Day."

Child Life, Rand McNally and Company, and Nancy Byrd Turner for "First

vii

"Rudolph Is Tired of the City" from *Bonzeville Boys and Girls* by Gwendolyn Brooks, copyright, (c), 1956, by Gwendolyn Brooks Blakely. Reprinted by permission of Harper and Row.

Helen B. Herford for "Stairs" by Oliver Herford.

Holt, Rinehart and Winston, Inc. for "Pockets," "If I Were a Pilgrim Child," "Tails," "Necks," "Smoke Animals," "Fire on the Hearth," and "The Freight Train" from *Story-Teller Poems* by Rowena Bennett, copyright, 1948, by Holt, Rinehart and Winston, Inc.

Holt, Rinehart and Winston, Inc. and Laurence Pollinger Ltd. for "Gathering Leaves," "Lodged," "Mending Wall," "The Gift Outright," "The Runaway," and "Stopping by Woods on a Snowy Evening" from *Complete Poems of Robert Frost*, copyright, 1923, 1928, 1930, 1939, by Holt, Rinehart and Winston, Inc., copyright, 1942, by Robert Frost, copyright renewed, 1951, (c), 1956, by Robert Frost; "Theme in Yellow," Young Sea," and "Lost" from *Chicago Poems* by Carl Sandburg, copyright, 1916, by Holt, Rinehart and Winston, Inc., copyright renewed, 1944, by Carl Sandburg. Reprinted by permission of the publishers.

Holt, Rinehart and Winston and The Society of Authors as the Literary Representative of the A. E. Housman Estate, and Messrs. Jonathan Cape, Ltd., publishers of A. E. Housman's *Collected Poems* for "Loveliest of Trees" from "A Shropshire Lad" — Authorized Edition — from *Complete Poems* by A. E. Housman, copyright, (c), 1959, by Holt, Rinehart and Winston, Inc.

Houghton Mifflin Company for "Night Clouds" from *What's O'Clock, 1925* by Amy Lowell; "Sea Shell" from *The Complete Poetical Works of Amy Lowell* by Amy Lowell; "A Song of Greatness" and "Charm for Going A-Hunting" from *Children Sing in the Far West* by Mary Austin; "Blue Smoke" from *Pool in the Meadow* by Frances Frost; "The Map" from *Poems* by Elizabeth Bishop; "A Nautical Ballad" from *Davy and the Goblin* by Charles Edward Carryl; "Christmas Bells," "Paul Revere's Ride," and "Hiawatha's Childhood" by Henry Wadsworth Longfellow from *Complete Poetical Works of Longfellow, 1882;* "The Enchanted Shirt" from *Poems* by John Hay; "A Bowl of October" from *A Change of Sky and Other Poems* by Helen Bevington; "Night Herding Song" by Harry Stephens from *Songs of the Cowboys* by N. Howard Thorp. Reprinted by permission of and arrangement with Houghton Mifflin Company, the authorized publishers.

Alfred A. Knopf, Inc. for "African Dance" from *The Dream Keeper* by Langston Hughes, copyright, 1932, by Alfred A. Knopf, Inc.; "Spanish Johnny" from *April Twilights* by Willa Cather, copyright, 1923, by Willa Cather, renewal copyright, 1951, by the Executors of the Estate of Willa Cather; "Grandmother's Visit" from *Jonathan Blake* by William

Poetry And
The Reader

Introduction

Poetry probably has been given as many definitions as there are people who have read it — and it is this personal aspect of the poetic experience that is unique and important. The variety of kinds of poems, and of the particular experiences that people associate with them, is so great that the word itself defies a narrow and formal definition.

This collection of poetry has been gathered for the intermediate-aged child to provide him with a sampling of the very wide range of poetic experiences. Acquaintanceship with these poems will begin to reveal the many aspects of poetic enjoyment, and the many ways in which poetry can be pleasing. As each new point of view, each vivid image, and each sensation becomes part of the child's experience, he will acquire new intellectual and emotional sensitivity to himself and to the world around him.

An Approach to Poetry

Adults often wonder what they can do to help children appreciate and enjoy poetry. They cannot "teach" poetry in the sense that they would teach arithmetic, but they can attempt to guide the child toward aesthetic awareness so that he can truly enjoy the poetry that he hears and reads. Their enthusiasm, ability to select appealing poetry, and willingness to experiment are the only prerequisites.

When children are very young, poetry is essentially an aural experience. They can hear rhythm and rhyme more easily than they can read it from a printed page, and they are dependent upon others for their enjoyment of poetry because they must listen rather than read to themselves. Children of the intermediate level are in a period of transition. Listening to poetry is still important, but the child is now able to read to himself. He can find selections that appeal to him, he can read to others and with others, and he is able to write his own poems.

One of the best ways to help children of this age group feel at home with poetry is to make sure poems are always available. The child who can refer to his own copy of an anthology is more likely to become familiar with many poems than the one who must borrow a book to find a poem.

A relaxed and natural frame of mind is best for the enjoyment of poetry — the audience open to new feelings and ideas rather than straining to analyze or understand. Luke Zilles' poem "Details" suggests the gentle, receptive mood of poetry:

> Let things touch your mind
> the same way one raindrop hits
> the pane just before
> it begins to rain,
> and the dust of the glass is
> streaked with one clean line.

Times for Poetry

Once an interest in poetry has been established, choosing the right poem is not difficult, and children are often able to make their own selections. Events or moods can often be occasions for poetry. Situations often arise into which poetry can be introduced, thereby taking advantage of immediate enthusiasm. When the poetic thought is closely related to the child's immediate feelings, his appreciation and enjoyment are usually deepest.

The role of poetry in a child's life can be greatly enhanced by a sensitive adult who is alert to situations in which it is appropriate. An outing in the country or a happy hike in the woods are probably the kinds of experiences Paul Laurence Dunbar had in mind when he wrote,

> And so I say
> On a summer's day,
> What's so fine as being a boy?
> Ha, Ha!

Poetry that is suitable for a particular occasion need not always deal with its literal details. A child who is sensitive might well feel a delicious tingle if, as he walked through the woods at dawn, he thought of Eleanor Farjeon's "Old Wife's Song."

> Once in a lifetime the white fawn run
> 'Twixt the falling of the moon and the rising of the sun.
> If you can trap one he'll grant you your boon
> 'Twixt the falling of the sun and the rising of the moon.

As children learn to relish the new sensations that the poet shares with them they may enjoy a more active participation in the poetic experience. Patience Strong's poem "Pictures in the Fire" describes a familiar but always enjoyable experience.

> What do you see in the fire tonight?
> I see the oddest things:
> A castle on a mountain-top:
> A bird with flaming wings.
> An old, old man, a gnome I think,
> A dwarf with pointed beard,
> A cottage with three chimney pots.
> A forest wild and wierd.

Reading or reciting this poem together might suggest to a family the pleasant activity of describing the fleeting fiery images before them.

The people who read, or better yet, recite these poems should be thoroughly familiar with them. Reading poetry aloud to oneself or into a tape recorder can be a very interesting and rewarding experience as well as an extremely helpful preparation for sharing it with others. One should strive to convey the mood and tempo of the poem without exaggeration and without forcing the pronunciation or rhythm.

Choosing Poetry

The child who has had an enthusiastic introduction to poetry, and who knows it not only as a way of expressing a thought, but as a fascinating, enjoyable, and many-faceted experience will generally come to appreciate and enjoy poetry by himself.

It is unwise to say that a particular poem is meant only for children. Rather, we can say that people appreciate the many aspects of poetry with varying degrees of sublety of understanding, and that these change as they grow and mature. For example, A. A. Milne's "If I Were King" has obvious appeal to children, but it can also be very precious to the adult, who can sense again, however fleetingly, the feeling that he once had on a rainy afternoon when he was alone with his thoughts. Or perhaps he can have the equally remarkable experience of recalling his childhood perceptions of this very poem. In ensuring children a familiarity with poetry, we are affording them a unique personal experience that they can enjoy and explore now, and relive and rediscover as they get older.

Poetry of the Everyday. Some of the poems that are easiest to enjoy and appreciate are those which deal, at least on the surface, with commonplace experiences. When children start with poems that appeal to their specific interests, they are very likely to find these leading naturally to new and different kinds of poems.

Jessie Orton Jones captures a universal experience in "I Can Climb Our Apple Tree" in describing a child's wonderment at an inchworm's climbing techniques compared with his own; and Amy Lowell's "Sea Shell, Sea Shell,/ Sing of the things you know so well" preserves the magic of a favorite and delightful seashore pastime.

Sometimes these common experiences can be given a new and charming aspect in the poetic retelling, as in the case of William Wise's "Grandmother's Visit" which describes the young child's glee at breaking all family taboos under the protective presence of an indulgent grandparent.

> This morning I was bad,
> But there's nothing to fear;
> My troubles are over
> When Grandmother's here!

Commonplace can become startling and new through the use of an unusual point of view. Carl Sandburg assumes the voice of all pumpkins when he writes, "I spot the hill/With yellow balls in autumn." Certainly the child's imagination is stirred when he identifies with the jack-o'-lantern:

> I am a jack-'o-lantern
> With terrible teeth
> And the children know
> I am fooling.

As he finds new experiences in the poet's description of the everyday world, the child can begin to develop the very precious ability to appreciate and enjoy the sights and sounds that accompany him on his daily routine — a miraculous experience as Walt Whitman describes it:

> Why, who makes much of a miracle?
> As to me I know of nothing else but miracles,
> Whether I walk the streets of Manhattan.
> Or dart my sight over the roofs of houses toward the sky . . .

Poetry of Childhood. The unique perceptions of childhood can be brought into focus and enjoyed where they might not otherwise have been appreciated. Rachel Field's poem "In Praise of Dust" expresses the sentiment of countless youngsters, and yet if they have ever recognized these feelings, they have probably dismissed them quickly with thoughts of dustcloths and brooms. How delightful then to read this poem and to think, "Why, that's just the way I feel!"

Just as much fun as drawing in the dust is writing on the frosty winter window pane. David McCord's description of one of the peculiarly child-like joys of winter in "The Frost Pane" gains additional appeal because of the poet's use of the language of the child.

Children's evident sensitivity to the moods of nature can also be expressed in the kind of empathic movement described in "On a Windy Day."

> And your wild, funny dance makes you laugh with glee
> Because you've so very much company.

Zhenya Gay's poem may well suggest to the child new ways of expressing his feelings about windy autumn days.

Poems on Special Subjects. Since animals are of interest to many children, there are many poems about them in this book. Yet within the category of animal poetry there are many variations. The child who has an enthusiasm for nature may find his interests treated with scientific accuracy and poetic beauty in poems such as the following by Marie de L. Welch:

> The chipmunk is compressed while the grim
> Wing-beat of a hawk passes;
> He is a chunk of turf, and his whiskers tremble on him
> In the manner of grasses.

Rachel Field captures the mystery of the migrating instinct in "Something Told the Wild Geese." T. S. Eliot abstracts something akin to the essence of the cat when he writes that

> The Naming of Cats is a difficult matter;
>   It isn't just one of your holiday games;
> You may think at first I'm as mad as a hatter
>   When I tell you, a cat must have THREE DIFFERENT NAMES.

The way in which an interest in one kind of poem can lead to an interest in several other kinds can be demonstrated as we extend the realm of animal poetry. For example, as the child reads Vachel Lindsay's "The Ghost of the Buffaloes," he will be introduced to one aspect of early American history as well as the grandeur and mystery of the great plains. The poem about the mule whose name is Sal describes the early years of the Erie Canal, another important and colorful phase of American history.

The child can then find other poems about early American life. He can begin to appreciate some of the Indian poems included here. "Corn-Grinding Song" expresses the Indian's reverence and respect for nature, upon which he depended so heavily. Mary Austin's transcription of the Chippewa Indian "Song of Greatness" carries a message of inspiration and seriousness of purpose that is especially appropriate to a young person whose life is before him.

> I too when my time comes
> Shall do mightily.

A number of the classics of poetic literature are also included in *The Reading of Poetry*. Shelley's "The Cloud" and Byron's "She Walks in Beauty" are among the finest poems in any collection and are included here because of the perfection of their music and the universality of their appeal, as are some of the poems which are more specifically associated with childhood, such as "Paul Revere's Ride" and "The Song of Hiawatha." The latter are closely related to the ballad form — one which would be most enjoyable for children who are fond of following the plots in stories.

Special Poetic Effects. One form of poetry that is often used to hold the interest of a reluctant participant is humorous poetry. The light-hearted limericks of Edward Lear have been favorites with several generations and are in a form that is fun to write as well as to read.

The blustering profanity of William Jay Smith's intemperate parrot (Lolloping Lumberjack! Old Baghdad! Cold Kamchatka! Hot heat pad!) is pure silliness at its best. And the ridiculous predicament of the girl who thought she had a foolproof way of remembering a multiplication fact in Anna Maria Pratt's "A Mortifying Mistake" will provide blessed relief to any child who has ever had to live with the tension of rote memorization preceding a test.

William Jay Smith plays with punctuation and achieves delightful results in "Poet."

> It, gives, you, hiccoughs, when, you, read.

A. A. Milne has so much fun with the rhyme and rhythm of words in "The Engineer" that the sense of the words themselves seems altogether secondary.

> Let it rain!
> Who cares?
> I've a train
> Upstairs,
> With a brake
> Which I make
> From a string
> Sort of thing.

This poem is a good example of the way in which rhyme, often one of the distinguishing features of poetry, can be used with special effectiveness.

Another important element of poetry is rhythm. Sometimes it is isolated for special emphasis as in Langston Hughes' "African Dance,"

> The low beating of the tom-toms,
> The slow beating of the tom-toms,
> Low . . . slow
> Slow . . . low —
> Stirs your blood.
> Dance!

New uses of words and word-combinations in poetry are often associated with E. E. Cummings. In his poem about spring, the squishy sounds of "mud-luscious" and the rounder tones of "puddle-wonderful" describe their subject in sounds as well as in words.

Sometimes, if one can dissociate oneself from the literal meaning of a poem, one can hear the story that the words tell beyond their literal meaning. The repetition in Liberty Hyde Bailey's "Farmer" imparts a sense of the monotony of the farmer's task. At the same time, one can almost see the motion of his sowing arm as it swings back and forth and his feet as they retread familiar earth.

> I hoe and plow
> I plow and hoe

These are certainly not the mechanized farming methods of the twentieth century.

Even silence itself can be described by the sounds of words. In Zhenya Gay's "Night Things are Soft and Loud" it is done through the repetition of *s* sounds:

> . . . a swish of high wild flowers as a soundless
> Small grass snake winds its way along.

Poetry and Self-Expression

Just as there are many kinds of poems, there are many ways in which the reading and recitation of poetry can be approached. Poetry can be read silently or aloud. It can be spoken chorally or responsively. It can be set to music or read with a musical or rhythmic accompaniment. Children can express their responses to poetry in pantomime, design, or dance.

Choral Speaking. Poetry is a sound as well as a thought, and it should be spoken as well as read. One of the most effective ways of hearing the music and rhythm of poetry is to speak it chorally or responsively. When voices are grouped or contrasted, the aural aspect of poetic beauty can be realized most fully.

The ballad set to music is an art form which is closely related to choral speaking and is a natural introduction to it. A familiar song like "The Erie Canal" has the elements of rhythm and repetition which are often emphasized in choral speaking. The fact that the lyrics represent the words and thoughts of one man affords the opportunity for dramatic expression — one of the aspects of choral speaking that appeal most directly to children.

A selection of poems which are especially appropriate for choral interpretation is included in the first section of this book, "Poetry for Choral Reading."

A family group, several playmates, or a small group of children might enjoy interpreting Louis Uutermeyer's adaptation of "Ten Brothers" chorally. It is an amusing poem and its story line makes the sequence easy to remember and follow. It also provides the fun of the sharp contrast between the drastic fate of each successive brother and the carefree, rollicking refrain.

Walter de la Mare's "Dream-Song" could well be adapted to responsive reading. One or two or three voices could answer each other or combine in expressing the mysterious impressionistic quality of the poem.

A very direct and uncomplicated selection with an appealing rhythmic pattern is "In the Fashion" by A. A. Milne. Because of the simplicity of its language and the repetitious element of its sequence, it would be appropriate for young children as well as for a group of mixed ages.

Walter de la Mare's "The Listeners" would be a challenging selection for a fairly large group to work on. Its ambiguity makes it a consistently fascinating subject for children, one that merits the familiarity that comes through repetition.

Sarojini Naidu's "In the Bazaars of Hyderabad" is essentially a question and answer sequence. Because of this, it is a suitable poem to read in either individual or choral contrapuntal responses.

It is often a good idea for the audience of a choral or responsive reading to follow the book as they listen. This will help them develop a sensitivity to the sounds of the poetry so that they can imagine them even when they are reading silently to themselves.

Interpreting Poetry. Music is an art form that is frequently compared with poetry, and the two often complement each other. It would be very natural and appropriate to precede or accompany the reading of John Burton Adams' "At a Cowboy Dance" with square dance or cowboy music.

Rhythm activities are also related to poetry. "Grasshopper Hop-o-the Grasses" by Grace Taber Hallock suggests a staccato jumping rhythm that children would probably enjoy responding to with fingers or toes.

Zhenya Gay's large and lumbering elephant would be fun to imitate in a rhythmic pantomime.

Another obvious and often pleasurable and worthwhile activity is to portray a poem graphically through drawing, painting, or collage. This is an activity that often helps children give their fullest attention to the meaning and imagery of a poem.

Analyzing Poetry. The question of how deeply a poem should be analyzed is raised frequently and merits careful consideration. Certainly it is interesting and useful to understand some of the poetic devices and images which help to enhance a particular poem. However, there is a very real danger in over-analyzing since confusion may often result. In an experience as intensely personal as poetry, there must be room for individual interpretation and receptivity, just as there is room for individual expression. Sometimes a poem is shorn of its beauty for a child, not because it has changed, but because it has been reduced to prosaic terms. Edna St. Vincent Millay's "The Unexplorer" warns against this danger.

> There was a road ran past our house
> Too lovely to explore.
> I asked my mother once — she said
> That if you followed where it led
> It brought you to a milk-man's door.
> (That's why I have not travelled more.)

Memorization of Poetry. Another consideration in dealing with poetry is whether or not it should be memorized. One of the wonderful aspects of memorization is that it enables one to recall a favorite poem and recite it to himself at the most apt moment — the moment at which it is recalled.

> Into my heart's treasury
> I slipped a coin
> That time cannot take
> Nor a thief purloin, —
> Oh, better than the minting
> Of a gold-crowned king
> Is the safe-kept memory
> Of a lovely thing.

> Sara Teasdale

However, it is indeed discouraging to know that one has the task of memorizing something that has been arbitrarily chosen and assigned. The deadly regularity of a "poetry time" or a "recitation" is enough to frighten all but the most gifted of memorizers. If outright memorization is to be required of children, it should be only occasionally and on a random schedule. It is best to remember that beloved poems are often memorized naturally, or with a minimum of effort as they become familiar, and that through repeated listening, reading, and choral speaking, a poem, like a song, can easily and naturally become part of one's "heart's treasury."

Writing Poetry. As children become familiar with poetry, they often wish to write it as well as to read and listen to it. As they begin to write, it is important to remember that the process of expression is most significant. More often than not, the novice poet brings to his work qualities of sincerity and simplicity. Carl Sandburg expresses the value of these qualities by describing the pitfalls that are present when they are ignored.

Look out how you use proud words.
When you let proud words go, it is not easy to call them back.
They wear long boots, hard boots; they walk off proud; they can't
     hear you calling —
Look out how you use proud words.

Sometimes children find it hard to take the initial steps of writing poetry without assistance. Perhaps these children would enjoy hearing Harry Behn's "Make Believe" and then making up their own additional verses.

I made believe fly
A bird so blue
It glowed like sky —
And up it flew!

Children who work best within some kind of structure might enjoy experimenting with the *haiku* form. These deceptively simple, unrhymed Japanese verses usually contain seventeen syllables and generally refer, directly or indirectly, to one of the seasons of the year.

A one-foot waterfall —
    it too makes noises,
        and at night is cool.

Contentment in Poverty by Issa

Summary

All of these suggestions have been made in an effort to help children find a place for poetry in their own lives and to help them appreciate it in their own way. Certainly a part of every person's experience with poetry is very personal and private. There should be ample room for individual preferences to be expressed and honored.

What kind of music does Tom like best?
Drums and fifes and the trumpet's bray.
What kind of music does Jenny like?
A whirling waltz-tune sweet and gay.

But the kind of music that Mary loves
Is any little gay or comical tune,
Played on a fiddle or clarinet
That skips like a leafy stream in June.

James Reeves

John Ciardi endorses the wisdom of encouraging individual preferences and the satisfaction that real love of poetry can bring when he says that "once one has learned to experience the poem as a poem, there inevitably arrives a sense that one is also experiencing himself as a human being."[1]

This collection contains poems of many different kinds: poems about childhood; poems about specific subjects, times, and places; poems of humor and of contemplation; and new and modern expressions using words, rhythms, and sound. They are poems selected for a particular age group, not because their appeal is a limited one, but because they are at once simple, clear, and lastingly beautiful. It is hoped that through the variety and quality of the poems included, there will be some poetic experience herein that will be meaningful to every child. For after all,

What is life, if, full of care,
We have no time to stand and stare.
Leisure by William Henry Davies

---

[1] John Ciardi, *How Does a Poem Mean?* (Boston: Houghton Mifflin Company, 1959) p. 667.

Contents

Poems

for

Choral

Reading

IF I WERE KING

A. A. Milne

I often wish I were King,
And then I could do anything.

If only I were King of Spain,
I'd take my hat off in the rain.

If only I were King of France,
I wouldn't brush my hair for aunts.

I think, if I were King of Greece,
I'd push things off the mantelpiece.

If I were King of Babylon,
I'd leave my button gloves undone.

If I were King of Timbuctoo,
I'd think of lovely things to do.

If I were King of anything,
I'd tell the soldiers, "I'm the King!"

MORAL SONG

John Farrar

Oh, so cool
In his deep green pool
Was a frog on a log one day!
He would blink his eyes
As he snapped at flies,
For his mother was away,
For his mother was away!

Now that naughty frog
Left his own home log
And started out to play.
He flipped and he flopped
And he never stopped
Till he reached the great blue bay,
Till he reached the great blue bay!

Alas, with a swish
Came a mighty fish,
And swallowed him where he lay.
Now it's things like this
That never miss
Little frogs who don't obey,
Little frogs who don't obey!

THE ENGINEER

A. A. Milne

Let it rain!
Who cares?
I've a train
Upstairs,
With a brake
Which I make
From a string
Sort of thing,
Which works
In jerks,
'Cos it drops
In the spring,
Which stops
With the string,
And the wheels
All stick
So quick
That it feels
Like a thing
That you make
With a brake,
Not string. . . .
So that's what I make,
When the day's all wet.
It's a good sort of brake
But it hasn't worked yet.

A BALLAD OF CHINA

Laura E. Richards

Her name was Dilliki Dolliki Dinah;
Niece she was to the Empress of China;
Fair she was as a morning of May,
When Hy Kokolorum stole her away.

He was a wizard, I'd have you know;
Wicked as weasels and black as a crow;
Lived in a castle a-top of a hill;
Had a panther whose name was Bill;

Used to ride him around and around,
Creeping and peeping close to the ground;
Working mischief wherever he could;
Nothing about him in any way good!

Saw the maiden one midsummer morn,
(Sweetest creature that ever was born!),
Creeped and peeped in his wizardly way,
Catched her and snatched her and stole her away!

All through China arose a cry:
"Some one has stolen our Dilliki Di!"
People gathered in every forum,
Crying, "It must be Hy Kokolorum!"

All the Barons in China land,
Ling the lofty and Bing the bland,
Kong the kingly and Bong the brave,
Vowed a vow to find and to save.

Darling Dilliki Dolliki Dinah
(Niece, you know, to the Empress of China;
Fair, you know, as a morning of May);
Whom Hy Kokolorum had stolen away.

Now in a kingly, ringly row,
Round and about the Hill they go,
Ling the lofty and Bing the bland,
Kong and Bong, and there they stand.

Weaving a weird and spinning a spell,
All with intent to quash and quell
Hy Kokolorum, worker of woe,
Wicked as weasels and black as a crow.

Dilliki Dinah was weeping her fill,
When stepped up softly the panther Bill;
Whispered, "If you will give me a kiss,
I'll turn your sorrow to bubbling bliss!"

She, to animals always kind,
Said, "No! Really? Well, I don't mind!"
Dropped a kiss on his nose so pink,
And—goodness gracious! What *do* you think?

He turned to a beautiful Golden King,
Crown and sceptre and everything!
Ran the old wizard through and through,
Saying, "Now there is an end of *you!*"

Caught the maiden up in his arms,
Broke through the net of spells and charms,
Cried to the Barons bold and brave,
"*I've* had the honor to find and save.

Darling Dilliki Dolliki Dinah,
Niece (I learn) to the Empress of China,
Fair (I swear) as a morning of May,
And she is my Queen from this very day!"

FARMER

Liberty Hyde Bailey

I hoe and I plow
I plow and I hoe
And the wind drives over the main.

I mow and I plant
I plant and I mow
While the sun burns hot on the plain.

I sow and I reap
I reap and I sow
And I gather the wind with the grain.

I go and I come
I come and I go
In the calm and the storm and the rain.

AFRICAN DANCE

Langston Hughes

The low beating of the tom-toms,
The slow beating of the tom-toms,
    Low . . . slow
    Slow . . . low —
Stirs your blood.
            Dance!
A night-veiled girl
    Whirls softly into a
    Circle of light.
Whirls softly . . . slowly,
Like a wisp of smoke around the fire —
    And the tom-toms beat,
    And the tom-toms beat,
And the low beating of the tom-toms
    Stirs your blood.

8

TEN BROTHERS

Adapted by Louis Untermeyer

We used to be ten brothers,
   Our business, it was wine.
One of us liked his trade too well —
   Now we're only nine.
Oh! Jascha, bring your fiddle
   And Sascha, take the air;
Come and play a little
   In the middle of the square.

We used to be nine brothers,
   Our business, it was freight.
One of us fell beneath a load —
   Now we're only eight.
Oh! Jascha, etc.

We used to be eight brothers,
   Our business was uneven;
One of us picked a lawyer's purse —
   Now we're only seven.
Oh! Jascha, etc.

We used to be seven brothers,
   Our business was with bricks.
One of us made a slight mistake —
   Now we're only six.
Oh! Jascha, etc.

We used to be six brothers,
    Our business did not thrive.
One of us found a wealthy widow —
    Now we're only five.
Oh! Jascha, etc.

We used to be five brothers,
    Our country went to war.
One of us traded at the front —
    Now we're only four.
Oh! Jascha, etc.

We used to be four brothers,
    Our business was at sea.
One of us bought himself a ship —
    Now we're only three.
Oh! Jascha, etc.

We used to be three brothers,
    Our business, it was glue.
One of us fell into the vat —
    Now we're only two.
Oh! Jascha, etc.

We used to be two brothers,
    We never could agree.
Our business was too small for both —
    Now there's only me.
Oh! Jascha, etc.

I am the last of the brothers,
　　Our business died away.
And since there's never enough to eat,
　　I perish every day.
　Oh! Jascha, etc.

MR. MOON

Bliss Carman

A Song of the Little People

O Moon, Mr. Moon,
When you comin' down?
Down on the hilltop,
Down in the glen,
Out in the clearin',
To play with little men?
Moon, Mr. Moon,
When you comin' down?

O Mr. Moon,
Hurry up along!
The reeds in the current
Are whisperin' slow;
The river's a-wimplin'
To and fro.
Hurry up along,
Or you'll miss the song!
Moon, Mr. Moon,
When you comin' down?

O Moon, Mr. Moon,
When you comin' down?
Down where the Good Folk
Dance in a ring,
Down where the Little Folk
Sing?
Moon, Mr. Moon,
When you comin' down?

NIGHT THINGS ARE SOFT AND LOUD

Zhenya Gay

Night things are soft and loud,
When the owl hoots the wind whispers.
When the katydids call
The moon shines quietly.
Soft and loud. The step of something on a twig,
And a swish of high wild flowers as a soundless
Small grass snake winds his way along.
A shirr hardly heard as the bat bobs and weaves with wide
    wing,
And the gentle tap of a branch on a window pane.
Tap-a-tap, soft and loud, as a moth's flutter or a cricket's call.
Let sleepers sleep deeply.
Night things are soft and loud and
Sleepers stir and stretch to the soft and loud sounds of
Night things.

PARROT

William Jay Smith

I bought me a Parrot in Trinidad
  And all the Parrot could say
When it got really good and mad,
Was something that sounded terribly bad:
Lolloping Lumberjack! Old Baghdad!
Cold Kamchatka! Hot heat pad!
  But then, when it felt gay,
The Parrot I bought in Trinidad
Would cry with all the voice it had:
Lovely Lollipop! Pink Doodad!
            Sweet Elephants!
            Hooray!

CHILD'S CAROL

Eleanor Farjeon

Here we come again, again, and here we come again!
Christmas is a single pearl swinging on a chain,
Christmas is a single flower in a barren wood,
Christmas is a single sail on the salty flood,
Christmas is a single star in the empty sky,
Christmas is a single song sung for charity.
Here we come again, again, to sing to you again,
Give a single penny that we may not sing in vain.

13

AN ELEPHANT IS AN ODD AFFAIR

Zhenya Gay

An elephant is an odd affair
With lots of skin and not much hair.
So very much skin that he always looks old
As it wrinkles down in fold after fold.
His ears are squarish and his feet are round.
His head's a long, long way from the ground.
His trunk is big but his tail is not.
Each eye is almost as small as a dot.
His four big legs are straight as high trees,
Except where they bend at his wrinkled knees.
An elephant's so large that I can't understand
Why he likes the small peanut I hold in my hand.

ON A WINDY DAY

Zhenya Gay

On a windy day in the country you see
The wildest dance that could ever be;
Tall trees wave and bow and bend,
Leaves do a two-step, end over end,
Grasses and reeds waltz down to the ground,
Bits of thistledown twirl round and round.
You yourself do a wild, funny dance

As the wind makes your feet spin in a lively prance.
And your wild, funny dance makes you laugh with glee
Because you've so very much company.

OLD WIFE'S SONG

Eleanor Farjeon

Once in a lifetime the white fawn run
'Twixt the falling of the moon and the rising of the sun.
If you can trap one he'll grant you your boon
'Twixt the falling of the sun and the rising of the moon.

Once in a lifetime the white falcon fly
'Twixt the clouding of the earth and the firing of the sky.
If you can snare one he'll give you your desire
'Twixt the waning of the cloud and the waxing of the fire.

You may ask what lies nearest to your heart and your mind,
From the kingdoms of the stars to the deserts of the wind,
Of the tongues of the birds the master shall you be,
And the wisdom of the roots, and the secrets of the sea.

But if you should fetter the fawn for good and all,
If with hood and jesses you keep the falcon thrall,
The wish you made for wisdom, for beauty, or for power,
Shall be to you a curse till your very last hour.

LAZY MARY, WILL YOU GET UP

Maud and Miska Petersham

Lazy Mary, will you get up,
Will you get up, will you get up?
Lazy Mary, will you get up,
Will you get up today?

What will you give me for breakfast
If I get up, if I get up?
What will you give me for breakfast
If I get up today?

A slice of bread and a cup of tea.

No, mother, I won't get up,
I won't get up, I won't get up.
No, mother, I won't get up,
I won't get up today.

A nice young man with rosy cheeks.

Yes, Mother, I will get up,
I will get up, I will get up,
Yes, Mother, I will get up,
I will get up today.

A BOY'S SUMMER SONG

Paul Laurence Dunbar

'Tis fine to play
In the fragrant hay,
And romp on the golden load;
To ride old Jack
To the barn and back,
Or tramp by a shady road.
To pause and drink,
At a mossy brink;
Ah, that is the best of joy,
And so I say
On a summer's day,
What's so fine as being a boy?
Ha, Ha!

With a line and hook
By a babbling brook,
The fisherman's sport we ply;
And list the song
Of the feathered throng
That flit in the branches nigh.
At last we strip
For a quiet dip;
Ah, that is the best of joy.
For this I say
On a summer's day,
What's so fine as being a boy?
Ha, Ha!

BUNG YER EYE

Stewart Edward White

I am a jolly shanty boy,
    As you will soon discover;
To all the dodges I am fly,
    A hustling pine woods rover.
A heavy hook it is my pride,
    An axe I well can handle.
To fell a tree or punch a bull
    Get rattling Danny Randle.
        Bung yer eye! bung yer eye!

I love a girl in Saginaw,
    She lives with her mother.
I defy all Michigan
    To find such another.
She's tall and slim, her hair is red,
    Her face is plump and pretty.
She's my daisy Sunday best-day girl,
    And her front name stands for Kitty.
        Bung yer eye! bung yer eye!

I took her to a dance one night,
    A mossback gave the bidding —
Silver Jack bossed the shebang,
    And Big Dan played the fiddle.
We danced and drank the livelong night
    With fights between the dancing,

18

Till Silver Jack cleaned out the ranch
And sent the mossbacks prancing.
Bung yer eye! bung yer eye!

THE RATTLESNAKE

John A. and Alan Lomax

A nice young ma-wan-wan
Lived on a hi-wi-will.
A nice young ma-wa-wan,
For I knew him we-we-well.

To my rattle, to my roo-rah-ree!

This nice young man-wa-wan
Went out to mo-wo-wow
To see if he-we-we
Could make a sho-wo-wow.

To my rattle, to my roo-rah-ree!

He scarcely mo-wo-wowed
Half round the fie-we-wield
Till up jumped — come a rattle,
come a sna-wa-wake,
And bit him on the he-we-weel.

19

To my rattle, to my roo-rah-ree!

He laid right dow-wo-wown
Upon the gro-wo-wound
And shut his ey-wy-wyes
And looked all aro-wo-wound.

To my rattle, to my roo-rah-ree!

"O pappy da-wa-wad,
Go tell my ga-wa-wal
That I'm a-goin' ter di-wi-wie,
For I know I sha-wa-wall."

To my rattle, to my roo-rah-ree!

"O pappy da-wa-wad,
Go spread the ne-wu-wus;
And here come Sa-wa-wall
Without her sho-woo-woos."

To my rattle, to my roo-rah-ree!

"O John, O Joh-wa-wahn,
Why did you go-wo-wo
Way down in the mea-we-we-dow
So far to mo-wo-wow?

20

To my rattle, to my roo-rah-ree!

"O Sal, O Sa-wa-wall,
Why don't you kno-wo-wow
When the grass gits ri-wi-wipe,
It must be mo-wo-woed?"

To my rattle, to my roo-rah-ree!

Come to all young gir-wi-wirls
And shed a te-we-wear
For this young ma-wa-wan
That died right he-we-were.

To my rattle, to my roo-rah-ree!

Come all young me-we-wen
And warning ta-wa-wake,
And don't get bi-wi-wit
By a rattlesna-wa-wake.

To my rattle, to my roo-rah-ree!

AT A COWBOY DANCE

John Burton Adams

Git yer little sage hens ready,
　　Trot 'em out upon the floor —
Line up there, you cusses! Steady!
　　Lively now! One couple more.
Shorty, shed that old sombrero;
　　Bronco, douse that cigarette;
Stop that cussin', Casimero,
　　'Fore the ladies! Now, all set!

S'lute yer ladies, all together!
　　Ladies opposite the same —
Hit the lumber with yer leathers!
　　Balance all, an' swing yer dame!
Bunch the heifers in the middle;
　　Circle stags an' do-se-do!
Pay attention to the fiddle!
　　Swing her round an' off you go!

First four forward! Back to places!
　　Second follow-shuffle back!
Now you've got it down to cases —
　　Swing 'em till their trotters crack!
Gents all right a-heel-and-toein'!
　　Swing 'em, kiss 'em if you kin —
On to next an' keep a-going'
　　Till you hit yer pards ag'in!

Gents to center; ladies round 'em,
  Form a basket; balance all!
Whirl yer gals to where you found 'em!
  Promenade around the hall!
Balance to yer pards an' trot 'em
  Round the circle double quick!
Grab an' kiss 'em while you've got 'em —
  Hold 'em to it if they kick!

Ladies, left hand to yer sonnies!
  Alaman! Grand right an' left!
Balance all, an' swing yer honeys —
  Pick 'em up an' feel their heft!
Promenade like skeery cattle —
  Balance all an' swing yer sweets!
Shake yer spurs an' make 'em rattle!
  Keno! Promenade to seats!

WEATHERS

Thomas Hardy

This is the weather the cuckoo likes,
        And so do I;
When showers benumble the chestnut spikes,
        And nestlings fly;
And the little brown nightingale bills his best,
And they sit outside the "Traveller's Rest,"
And maids come forth sprig-muslin drest,
And citizens dream of the South and West,
        And so do I.

This is the weather the shepherd shuns,
      And so do I;
When beeches drip in browns and duns,
      And thresh, and ply;
And hill-hid tides throb, throe on throe,
And meadow rivulets overflow,
And drops on gate-bars hang in a row,
And rooks in families homeward go,
      And so do I.

DREAM-SONG

Walter de la Mare

Sunlight, moonlight,
Twilight, starlight —
Gloaming at the close of day,
And an owl calling,
Cool dews falling
In a wood of oak and may.

Lantern-light, taper-light,
Torchlight, no-light;
Darkness at the shut of day,
And lions roaring,
Their wrath pouring
In wild places far away.

Elf-light, bat-light,
Touchwood-light and toad-light,
And the sea a shimmering gloom of grey,

24

And a small face smiling
In a dream's beguiling
In a world of wonders far away.

FEATHER OR FUR

John Becker

When you watch for
Feather or fur
Feather or fur
Do not stir
Do not stir.

Feather or fur
Come crawling
Creeping
Some come peeping
Some by night
And some by day.
Most come gently
All come softly
Do not scare
A friend away.

When you watch for
Feather or fur
Feather or fur
Do not stir
Do not stir.

THE COROMANDEL FISHERS

Sarojini Naidu

Rise, brothers, rise; the waking skies pray to the morning
light,
The wind lies asleep in the arms of the dawn like a child that
has cried all night;
Come, let us gather our nets from the shore and set our
catamarans free
To capture the leaping wealth of the tide, for we are the
kings of the sea!

No longer delay, let us hasten away in the track of the seagull's call,
The sea is our mother, the cloud is our brother, the waves
are our comrades all,
What though we toss at the fall of the sun where the hand
of the sea-god drives?
He who holds the storm by the hair will hide in his breast
our lives.

Sweet is the shade of the cocoanut glade and the scent of the
mango grove,
And sweet are the sands at the fall of the moon with the
sound of the voices we love;
But sweeter, O brothers, the kiss of the spray, and the dance
of the wild foam's glee;
Row, brothers, row, to the blue of the verge, where the low
sky mates with the sea.

THE TWELVE DAYS OF CHRISTMAS

Unknown

On the first day of Christmas my true love sent to me a partridge in a pear tree.

On the second day of Christmas my true love sent to me two turtledoves, and a partridge in a pear tree.

On the third day of Christmas my true love sent to me three French hens, two turtledoves, and a partridge in a pear tree.

On the fourth day of Christmas my true love sent to me four calling birds, three French hens, two turtledoves, and a partridge in a pear tree.

On the fifth day of Christmas my true love sent to me five gold rings, four calling birds, three French hens, two turtledoves, and a partridge in a pear tree.

On the sixth day of Christmas my true love sent to me six geese a-laying, five gold rings, four calling birds, three French hens, two turtledoves, and a partridge in a pear tree.

On the seventh day of Christmas my true love sent to me seven swans a-swimming, six geese a-laying, five gold rings, four calling birds, three French hens, two turtledoves, and a partridge in a pear tree.

On the eighth day of Christmas my true love sent to me eight maids a-milking, seven swans a-swimming, six geese a-laying, five gold rings, four calling birds, three French hens, two turtledoves and a partridge in a pear tree.

On the ninth day of Christmas my true love sent to me nine ladies dancing, eight maids a-milking, seven swans a-swimming, six geese a-laying, five gold rings, four calling birds, three French hens, two turtledoves, and a partridge in a pear tree.

On the tenth day of Christmas my true love sent to me ten lords a-leaping, nine ladies dancing, eight maids a-milking, seven swans a-swimming, six geese a-laying, five gold rings, four calling birds, three French hens, two turtledoves and a partridge in a pear tree.

On the eleventh day of Christmas my true love sent to me eleven pipers piping, ten lords a-leaping, nine ladies dancing, eight maids a-milking, seven swans a-swimming, six geese a-laying, five gold rings, four calling birds, three French hens, two turtledoves, and a partridge in a pear tree.

On the twelfth day of Christmas my true love sent to me twelve drummers drumming, eleven pipers piping, ten lords a-leaping, nine ladies dancing, eight maids a-milking, seven swans a-swimming, six geese a-laying, five gold rings, four calling birds, three French hens, two turtledoves, and a partridge in a pear tree.

I SAW THREE SHIPS

Unknown

> I saw three ships come sailing in,
>   On Christmas day, on Christmas day,
> I saw three ships come sailing in,
>   On Christmas day, in the morning.

Pray whither sailed those ships all three
    On Christmas day, on Christmas day?
Pray whither sailed those ships all three
    On Christmas day, in the morning.

Oh, they sailed into Bethlehem
    On Christmas day, on Christmas day;
Oh, they sailed into Bethlehem
    On Christmas day, in the morning.

And all the bells on earth shall ring
    On Christmas day, on Christmas day;
And all the bells on earth shall ring
    On Christmas day, in the morning.

And all the angels in heaven shall sing,
    On Christmas day, on Christmas day;
And all the angels in heaven shall sing,
    On Christmas day, in the morning.

And all the souls on earth shall sing
    On Christmas day, on Christmas day;
And all the souls on earth shall sing
    On Christmas day, in the morning.

IN JUST—SPRING

E. E. Cummings

       in Just-
       spring   when the world is mud-
       luscious the little
       lame balloonman

       whistles   far   and wee

       and eddieandbill come
       running from marbles and
       piracies and it's
       spring

       when the world is puddle-wonderful

       the queer
       old balloonman whistles
       far   and   wee
       and bettyandisbel come dancing

       from hop-scotch and jump-rope and

       it's
       spring

                    and
                          the

                              goat-footed

                    balloonMan   whistles
                    far
                    and
                    wee

IN THE FASHION

A. A. Milne

A lion has a tail and a very fine tail,
And so has an elephant, and so has a whale,
And so has a crocodile, and so has a quail —
    They've all got tails but me.

If I had sixpence I would buy one;
I'd say to the shopman, "Let me try one;"
I'd say to the elephant, "This is *my* one";
    They'd all come round to see.

Then I'd say to the lion, "Why, *you've* got a tail!
And so has the elephant, and so has the whale!
And look! There's a crocodile. He's got a tail!
    You've all got tails like me!"

31

TWO OLD CROWS

Vachel Lindsay

Two old crows sat on a fence rail.
Two old crows sat on a fence rail,
Thinking of effect and cause,
Of weeds and flowers,
And nature's laws.
One of them muttered, one of them stuttered,
One of them stuttered, one of them muttered.
Each of them thought far more than he uttered.
One crow asked the other crow a riddle.
One crow asked the other crow a riddle:
The muttering crow
Asked the stuttering crow,
"Why does a bee have a sword to his fiddle?
Why does a bee have a sword to his fiddle?"
"Bee-cause," said the other crow,
"Bee-cause,
B B B B B B B B B B B B B B-cause."
Just then a bee flew close to their rail: —
"Buzzzzzzzzzzzzzzzzzzz zzzzzzzzz zzzzzzzzzzzzzzzz
    ZZZZZZZZ."
And those two black crows
Turned pale,
And away those crows did sail.
Why?
B B B B B B B B B B B B B B-cause.
B B B B B B B B B B B B B B-cause.
"Buzzzzzzzzzzzzzzzzzzz zzzzzzzzz zzzzzzzzzzzzzzzz
    ZZZZZZZZ."

SEA FEVER

John Masefield

I must go down to the seas again, to the lonely sea and the
sky,
And all I ask is a tall ship and a star to steer her by;
And the wheel's kick and the wind's song and the white sail's
shaking,
And the gray mist on the sea's face, and a gray dawn
breaking.

I must go down to the seas again, for the call of the running
tide
Is a wild call and a clear call that may not be denied;
And all I ask is a windy day with the white clouds flying,
And the flung spray and the blown spume, and the seagulls
crying.

I must go down to the seas again, to the vagrant gipsy life,
To the gull's way and the whale's way where the wind's like
a whetted knife;
And all I ask is a merry yarn from a laughing fellow-rover,
And a quiet sleep and a sweet dream when the long trick's
over.

THE LISTENERS

Walter de la Mare

"Is anybody there?" said the Traveller,
   Knocking on the moonlit door;
And his horse in the silence champed the grasses
   Of the forest's ferny floor:
And a bird flew up out of the turret,
   Above the Traveller's head:
And he smote upon the door again a second time;
   "Is anybody there?" he said.
But no one descended to the Traveller;
   No head from the leaf-fringed sill
Leaned over and looked into his grey eyes,
   Where he stood perplexed and still.
But only a host of phantom listeners
   That dwelt in the lone house then
Stood listening to the quiet of the moonlight
   To that voice from the world of men:
Stood thronging the faint moonbeams on the dark stair,
   That goes down to the empty hall,
Hearkening in an air stirred and shaken
   By the lonely Traveller's call.
And he felt in his ear that strangeness,
   Their stillness answering his cry,
While his horse moved, cropping the turf,
   'Neath the starred and leafy sky;
For he suddenly smote on the door, even
   Louder, and lifted his head: —
"Tell them I came, and no one answered,

That I kept my word," he said.
Never the least stir made the listeners,
  Though every word he spake
Fell echoing through the shadowiness of the still house
  From the one man left awake:
Ay, they heard his foot upon the stirrup,
  And the sound of iron on stone,
And how the silence surged softly backward,
  When the plunging hoofs were gone.

GRANDFATHER FROG

Louise Seaman Bechtel

Fat green frog sits by the pond,
Big frog, bull frog, grandfather frog.
Croak-croak-croak.
Shuts his eye, opens his eye,
Rolls his eye, winks his eye,
Waiting for
A little fat fly.
Croak, croak.
I go walking down by the pond,
I want to see the big green frog,
I want to stare right in his eye,
Rolling, winking, funny old eye.
But oh! he hears me coming by.
Croak-croak —
SPLASH!

BROWN BEAR'S HONEY SONG

Kathryn Jackson

Apple blossom is crystal white
    (But I don't care a tittle, I don't care a mite),
Buckwheat honey's 'most as dark as me
    (But I don't care a bittle, I don't care a bee),
Gooseberry honey is a pale, pale green
    (But I don't care a button, I don't care a bean),
Golden is the honey, and honey is sweet —
And never mind the color when it's time to eat!

CHIPMUNK

Marie de L. Welch

When he runs hunting the chipmunk stretches
To a stripe over the wood's ground;
He has the sun's style of flickering; he matches
The half-shadowy places where nuts are found.

The chipmunk is compressed while the grim
Wing-beat of a hawk passes;
He is a chunk of turf, and his whiskers tremble on him
In the manner of grasses.

GOODY O'GRUMPITY

Carol Ryrie Brink

When Goody O'Grumpity baked a cake
The tall reeds danced by the mournful lake,
The pigs came nuzzling out of their pens,
The dogs ran sniffling and so did the hens,
And the children flocked by dozens and tens.
They came from the north, the east and the south
With wishful eyes and watering mouth,
And stood in a crowd about Goody's door,
Their muddy feet on her sanded floor.
And what do you s'pose they came to do!
Why, to lick the dish when Goody was through!
And throughout the land went such a smell
Of citron and spice — no words can tell
How cinnamon bark and lemon rind,
And round, brown nutmegs grated fine
A wonderful haunting perfume wove,
Together with allspice, ginger and clove,
When Goody but opened the door of her stove.
The children moved close in a narrowing ring,
They were hungry — as hungry as bears in the spring;
They said not a word, just breathed in the spice,
And at last when the cake was all golden and nice,
Goody took a great knife and cut each a slice.

HORSE

Elizabeth Madox Roberts

His bridle hung around the post;
The sun and the leaves made spots come down;
I looked close at him through the fence;
The post was drab and he was brown.

His nose was long and hard and still,
And on his lip were specks like chalk.
But once he opened up his eyes,
And he began to talk.

He didn't talk out with his mouth;
He didn't talk with words or noise.
The talk was there along his nose;
It seemed and then it was.

He said the day was hot and slow,
And he said he didn't like the flies;
They made him have to shake his skin,
And they got drowned in his eyes.

He said that drab was just about
The same as brown, but he was not
A post, he said, to hold a fence.
"I'm horse," he said, "that's what!"

And then he shut his eyes again.
As still as they had been before.
He said for me to run along
And not to bother him any more.

THE FROST PANE

David McCord

What's the good of breathing
On the window
Pane
In summer?
You can't make a frost
On the window pane
In summer.
You can't write a
Nalphabet,
You can't draw a
Nelephant;
You can't make a smudge
With your nose
In summer.

Lots of good, breathing
On the window
Pane
In winter.

You can make a frost
On the window pane
In winter.
A white frost, a light frost,
A thick frost, a quick frost,
A write me-out-a-picture frost
Across
The pane
In winter.

THE BAD KITTENS

Elizabeth Coatsworth

You may call, you may call
But the little black cats won't hear you.
The little black cats are maddened
    By the bright green light of the moon;
They are whirling and running and hiding,
They are wild who were once so confiding,
They are crazed when the moon is riding —
    You will not catch the kittens soon.
They care not for saucers of milk,
They think not of pillows of silk;
Your softest, crooningest call
    Is less than the buzzing of flies.
They are seeing more than you see,
They are hearing more than you hear,
And out of the darkness they peer
    With a goblin light in their eyes!

SPANISH JOHNNY

Willa Cather

> The old West, the old time,
>   The old wind singing through
> The red, red grass a thousand miles —
>   And, Spanish Johnny, you!
> He'd sit beside the water ditch
>   When all his herd was in,
> And never mind a child, but sing
>   To his mandolin.

> The big stars, the blue night,
>   The moon-enchanted lane;
> The olive man who never spoke,
>   But sang the songs of Spain.
> His speech with men was wicked talk —
>   To hear it was a sin;
> But those were golden things he said
>   To his mandolin.

> The gold songs, the gold stars,
>   The word so golden then;
> And the hand so tender to a child —
>   Had killed so many men.
> He died a hard death long ago
>   Before the Road came in —
> The night before he swung, he sang
>   To his mandolin.

A TRAGIC STORY

William Makepeace Thackeray

There lived a sage in days of yore,
And he a handsome pigtail wore;
But wondered much and sorrowed more,
    Because it hung behind him.

He mused upon this curious case,
And swore he'd change the pigtail's place,
And have it hanging at his face,
    Not dangling there behind him.

Said he, "The mystery I've found —
I'll turn me round" — he turned him round,
    But still it hung behind him.

Then round and round, and out and in,
All day the puzzled sage did spin;
In vain — it mattered not a pin —
    The pigtail hung behind him.

And right and left, and roundabout,
And up and down and in and out
He turned; but still the pigtail stout
    Hung steadily behind him.

And though his efforts never slack,
And though he twist, and twirl, and tack,
Alas! still faithful to his back,
    The pigtail hangs behind him.

AN OLD WOMAN OF THE ROADS

Padraic Colum

O, to have a little house!
To own the hearth and stool and all!
The heaped-up sods upon the fire,
The pile of turf against the wall!

To have a clock with weights and chains
And pendulum swinging up and down!
A dresser filled with shining delph,
Speckled and white and blue and brown!

I could be busy all the day
Cleaning and sweeping hearth and floor,
And fixing on their shelf again
My white and blue and speckled store!

I could be quiet there at night
Beside the fire and by myself,
Sure of a bed, and loth to leave
The ticking clock and the shining delph!

Och! but I'm weary of mist and dark,
And roads where there's never a house nor bush,
And tired I am of bog and road
And the crying wind and the lonesome hush!

And I am praying to God on high,
And I am praying Him night and day,
For a little house — a house of my own —
Out of the wind's and the rain's way.

MOLE

William Jay Smith

Jiminy Jiminy Jukebox! Wheatcakes! Crumbs!
Blow the bugle! Roll the drums!
Hide beneath the delphiniums!

Trim my whiskers! Bless my soul!
Here comes a big brown one-eyed Mole
All wound up like a jelly roll,
Too fat to waddle back to his hole!

Jiminy Jiminy Jukebox! Wheatcakes! Crumbs!
Howling Hatpin!
Here
he

comes!

THE WORLD HAS HELD GREAT HEROES

Kenneth Grahame

The world has held great Heroes,
    As history-books have showed;
But never a name to go down to fame
    Compared with that of Toad!

The clever men at Oxford
    Know all that there is to be knowed.
But they none of them know one half as much
    As intelligent Mr. Toad!

The animals sat in the Ark and cried,
    Their tears in torrents flowed.
Who was it said, "There's land ahead?"
    Encouraging Mr. Toad!

The Army all saluted
    As they marched along the road.
Was it the King? Or Kitchener?
    No. It was Mr. Toad!

The Queen and her Ladies-in-waiting
    Sat at the window and sewed.
She cried, "Look! who's that *handsome* man?"
    They answered, "Mr. Toad."

THE GHOST OF THE BUFFALOES

Vachel Lindsay

Last night at black midnight I woke with a cry,
The windows were shaking, there was thunder on high,
The floor was atremble, the door was ajar,
White fires, crimson fires, shone from afar.
I rushed to the dooryard. The city was gone.
My home was a hut without orchard or lawn.
It was mud-smear and logs near a whispering stream,
Nothing else built by man could I see in my dream. . . .
Then. . . .
Ghost-kings came headlong, row upon row,
Gods of the Indians, torches aglow.

They mounted the bear and the elk and the deer,
And eagles gigantic, aged and sere,
They rode long-horn cattle, they cried "A-la-la."
They lifted the knife, the bow, and the spear,
They lifted ghost-torches from dead fires below,
The midnight made grand with the cry "A-la-la."
The midnight made grand with a red-god charge,
A red-god show,
A red-god show,
"A-la-la, a-la-la, a-la-la, a-la-la."

With bodies like bronze, and terrible eyes
Came the rank and the file, with catamount cries,
Gibbering, yipping, with hollow-skull clacks,

46

Riding white bronchos with skeleton backs,
Scalp-hunters, beaded and spangled and bad,
Naked and lustful and foaming and mad,
Flashing primeval demoniac scorn,
Blood-thirst and pomp amid darkness reborn,
Power and glory that sleep in the grass
While the winds and the snows and the great rains pass.
They crossed the gray river, thousands abreast,
They rode in infinite lines to the west,
Tide upon tide of strange fury and foam,
Spirits and wraiths, the blue was their home,
The sky was their goal where the star-flags were furled,
And on past those far golden splendors they whirled.
They burned to dim meteors, lost in the deep.
And I turned in dazed wonder, thinking of sleep.

And the wind crept by
Alone, unkempt, unsatisfied,
The wind cried and cried —
Muttered of massacres long past,
Buffaloes on shambles vast . . .
An owl said: "Hark, what is a-wing?"
I heard a cricket carolling,
I heard a cricket carolling,
I heard a cricket carolling.

Then. . . .
Snuffing the lightning that crashed from on high
Rose royal old buffaloes, row upon row.
The lords of the prairie came galloping by.
And I cried in my heart "A-la-la, a-la-la,

A red-god show,
A red-god show,
A-la-la, a-la-la, a-la-la, a-la-la."

Buffaloes, buffaloes, thousands abreast,
A scourge and amazement, they swept to the west.
With black bobbing noses, with red rolling tongues,
Coughing forth steam from their leather-wrapped lungs,
Cows with their calves, bulls big and vain,
Goring the laggards, shaking the mane,
Stamping flint feet, flashing moon eyes.
Pompous and owlish, shaggy and wise.
Like sea-cliffs and caves resounded their ranks
With shoulders like waves, and undulant flanks.
Tide upon tide of strange fury and foam,
Spirits and wraiths, the blue was their home,
The sky was their goal where the star-flags are furled,
And on past those far golden splendors they whirled.
They burned to dim meteors, lost in the deep,
And I turned in dazed wonder, thinking of sleep.

THE ZEBRA DUN

American Cowboy Ballad

We were camped on the plains at the head of the Cimarron
When along came a stranger and stopped to arger some,
He seemed so very foolish that we began to look around,
We thought he was a greenhorn that had just 'scaped from
  town.

We asked if he'd been to breakfast; he hadn't had a smear,
So we opened up the chuck-box and bade him have his share.
He took a cup of coffee and some biscuits and some beans,
And then began to talk and tell about foreign kings and
  queens, —

About the Spanish war and the fighting on the seas
With guns as big as steers and ramrods big as trees, —
And about Old Paul Jones, a mean, fighting son of a gun,
Who was the grittiest cuss that ever pulled a gun.

Such an educated feller, his thoughts just came in herds,
He astonished all them cowboys with them jaw-breaking
  words.
He just kept on talking till he made the boys all sick,
And they begin to look around just how to play a trick.

He said that he had lost his job upon the Santa Fe
And was going across the plains to strike the 7-D.

49

He didn't say how come it, some trouble with the boss,
But said he'd like to borrow a nice fat saddle hoss.

This tickled all the boys to death, they laughed down in their
    sleeves, —
"We'll lend you a horse just as fresh and fat as you please."
Shorty grabbed a lariat and roped the Zebra Dun.
Turned him over to the stranger and waited for the fun.

Old Dunny was a rocky outlaw that had grown so awful wild
That he could paw the white out of the moon every jump
    for a mile.
Old Dunny stood right still, — as if he didn't know, —
Until he was saddled and ready to go.

When the stranger hit the saddle, old Dunny quit the earth,
And traveled right straight up for all that he was worth.
A-pitching and a-squealing, a-having wall-eyed fits,
His hind feet perpendicular, his front ones in the bits.

We could see the tops of the mountains under Dunny every
    jump,
But the stranger he was growed there just like the camel's
    hump;
The stranger sat upon him and curled his black mustache
Just like a summer boarder waiting for his hash.

He thumped him in the shoulders and spurred him when he
    whirled,

To show them flunky punchers that he was the wolf of the
world.
When the stranger had dismounted once more upon the
ground,
We knew he was a thoroughbred and not a gent from town.

The boss who was standing round, a-watching of the show,
Walked right up to the stranger and told him he needn't
go, —
"If you can use the lasso like you rode old Zebra Dun,
You're the man I've been looking for ever since the year of
one."

Oh, he could twirl the lariat and he didn't do it slow,
He could catch them forefeet nine out of ten for any kind of
dough.
And when the herd stampeded he was always on the spot
And set them to nothing, like the boiling of a pot.

There's one thing and a shore thing I've learned since I've
been born,
That every educated feller ain't a plumb greenhorn.

TWELVE OXEN

Unknown

I have twelve oxen that be fair and brown,
And they go a-grazing down by the town.
With hey! with how! with hey!
Sawest you not mine oxen, you little pretty boy?

I have twelve oxen, and they be fair and white,
And they go a-grazing down by the dyke.
  With hey! with how! with hey!
Sawest you not mine oxen, you little pretty boy?

I have twelve oxen, and they be fair and black,
And they go a-grazing down by the lake.
  With hey! with how! with hey!
Sawest you not mine oxen, you little pretty boy?

I have twelve oxen, and they be fair and red,
And they go a-grazing down by the mead.
  With hey! with how! with hey!
Sawest you not mine oxen, you little pretty boy?

STOPPING BY WOODS ON A SNOWY EVENING

Robert Frost

Whose woods these are I think I know.
His house is in the village though;
He will not see me stopping here
To watch his woods fill up with snow.

My little horse must think it queer
To stop without a farmhouse near
Between the woods and frozen lake
The darkest evening of the year.

He gives his harness bells a shake
To ask if there is some mistake.
The only other sound's the sweep
Of easy wind and downy flake.

The woods are lovely, dark and deep,
But I have promises to keep,
And miles to go before I sleep,
And miles to go before I sleep.

PEG-LEG'S FIDDLE

Bill Adams

I've a pal called Billy Peg-Leg, with one leg a wood leg,
And Billy he's a ship's cook, and lives upon the sea;
And, hanging by his griddle,
Old Billy keeps a fiddle,
For fiddling in the dog-watch, when the moon is on the sea.

We takes our luck wi' tough ships, wi' fast ships, wi' free
  ships,
We takes our luck wi' any ship to sign away for sea;
We takes our trick wi' the best o' them,
And sings our song wi' the rest o' them,
When the bell strikes the dog-watch, and the moon is on the
  sea.

You'd ought to see them tops'ls, them stays'ls, them stuns'ls,
When the moon's a-shinin' on them along a liftin' sea;
Hear the dandy bo'sun say,
"Peg-Leg, make that fiddle play,
And we'll dance away the dog-watch, while the moon is on
   the sea."

Then it's fun to see them dancin', — them bow-legged sailors
   dancin',
To the tune o' Peg-Leg's fiddle, a-fiddlin' fast and free,
It's fun to watch old Peg-Leg,
A'waltzin' wi' his wood leg,
When bo'sun takes the fiddle, so Peg can dance wi' me.

The moon is on the water, the dark moon-glimmered water,
The night wind pipin' plaintively along a liftin' sea;
There ain't no female wimmen.
No big beer glasses brimmin'.
There's just the great sea's glory, and Billy Peg an' me.

We takes our luck wi' tough ships, wi' fast ships, wi' free
   ships,
We takes our luck wi' any ship to sign away to sea;
We takes our trick wi' the best o' them,
And sings our song wi' the rest o' them,
When the bell strikes the dog-watch, and the moon is on the
   sea.

THE KITE

Harry Behn

How bright on the blue
Is a kite when it's new!

With a dive and a dip
It snaps its tail

Then soars like a ship
With only a sail

As over tides
Of wind it rides,

Climbs to the crest
Of a gust and pulls,

Then seems to rest
As wind falls.

When string goes slack
You wind it back

And run until
A new breeze blows

And its wings fill
And up it goes!

How bright on the blue
Is a kite when it's new!

But a raggeder thing
You never will see

When it flaps on a string
In the top of a tree.

IN THE BAZAARS OF HYDERABAD

Sarojini Naidu

What do you sell, O ye merchants?
Richly your wares are displayed.
Turbans of crimson and silver,
Tunics of purple brocade,
Mirrors with panels of amber,
Daggers with handles of jade.

What do you weigh, O ye vendors?
Saffron and lentil and rice.
What do you grind, O ye maidens?
Sandalwood, henna, and spice,
What do you call, O ye pedlars?
Chessmen and ivory dice.

What do you make, O ye goldsmiths?
Wristlet and anklet and ring,
Bells for the feet of blue pigeons,
Frail as a dragon-fly's wing,
Girdles of gold for the dancers,
Scabbards of gold for the king.

What do you cry, O ye fruitmen?
Citron, pomegranate, and plum.
What do you play, O musicians?
Cither, sarangi, and drum.
What do you chant, O magicians?
Spells for aeons to come.

What do you weave, O ye flower-girls
With tassels of azure and red?
Crowns for the brow of a bridegroom,
Chaplets to garland his bed.
Sheets of white blossoms new-gathered
To perfume the sleep of the dead.

*Sound
and
Song*

SLEEP IMPRESSION

Carl Sandburg

> The dark blue of early autumn
> ran on the early autumn sky
> in the fields of yellow moon harvest.
> I slept, I almost slept,
> I said listening:
> Trees you have leaves rustling like rain
> When there is no rain.

LAKE WINNIPESAUKEE

Olive Driver

The early Indians were our first poets —
They who lived with wind and rain and sun
Looked on the stars, the mountains and the lakes
And named them in their own expressive language;
Having no written tongue, they wrote no poems
But wove their imagery and love of beauty
Into their common speech
In simple similes and metaphors
That would have done a Keats or Shelley justice.

There is a sunny lake in old New Hampshire
Set with three hundred islands

60

Like tiny clouds on a great patch of sky
Fallen to earth between low, rugged hills;
The Indians called this lake "Winnipesaukee,"
Which is, translated, "The Smile of the Great Spirit";
If it be true, as I have heard it said,
That common speech reflects a people's nature,
Then I believe I know this simple people
Quite well, though they themselves have long since vanished.

Our early forebears, worthy folks and true,
But lacking in that fine, poetic vision,
Would, without doubt, have named these sunny waters
For size, perhaps, "The Great Lake,"
Or for some dignitary, Edward or James or Henry;
I'm glad they chose to keep the older name,
The simple, lovely name the Indians gave it,
That speaks the timeless, universal language
Of beauty and of reverence;
I'm glad we use the ancient name today —
WINNIPESAUKEE, THE SMILE OF THE GREAT SPIRIT.

SPRING BREEZE

Buson

These morning airs —
    one can see them stirring
    caterpillar hairs!

61

THE RED PEONY

Buson

> It falls, the peony —
>   and upon each other lie
>   petals, two or three.

HAZE

Buson

> Morning haze:
>   as in a painting of a dream,
>   men go their ways.

THE SNAKE

Kyoshi

> A snake! Though it passes,
>   eyes that had glared at me
>   stay in the grasses.

THE CAMELLIA

Bashō

As it fell,
water poured out —
the camellia-bell.

LEAVING THE HOUSE OF A FRIEND

Bashō

Out comes the bee
from deep among peony pistils —
oh, so reluctantly!

THE AUTUMN STORM

Bashō

Wild boars and all
are blown along with it —
storm-wind of fall!

HARBINGERS

Bashō

Spring too, very soon!
    They are setting the scene for it —
        plum tree and moon.

THE STILLNESS

Bashō

So still:
    into rocks it pierces —
        the locust-shrill.

THE END OF SUMMER

Bashō

The beginning of fall:
    the ocean, the rice fields —
        one green for all!

CONTENTMENT IN POVERTY

Issa

A one-foot waterfall —
it too makes noises,
and at night is cool.

THE FIREFLY

Issa

A giant firefly:
that way, this way, that way, this —
and it passes by.

LATE SHOW

Issa

Seeming as though
this must be the last of it —
so much spring snow!

SUMMER NIGHT

Ranko

Summer night:
from cloud to cloud the moon
is swift in flight.

THE STORM

Chora

A storm-wind blows
out from among the grasses
the full moon grows.

HARVEST MOON

Ryota

So brilliant a moonshine:
if ever I am born again —
a hilltop pine!

66

SPRING IN MY HUT

Sodo

> My hut in spring!
> True, there is nothing in it —
> there is Everything.

COOLNESS IN SUMMER

Ryusui

> In all this cool
> is the moon also sleeping?
> There, in the pool?

THE CLOUD

Percy Bysshe Shelley

I bring fresh showers for the thirsting flowers,
    From the seas and the streams;
I bear light shade for the leaves when laid
    In their noonday dreams.
From my wings are shaken the dews that waken
    The sweet buds every one,

When rocked to rest on their mother's breast,
    As she dances about the sun.
I wield the flail of the lashing hail,
    And whiten the green plains under,
And then again I dissolve it in rain,
    And laugh as I pass in thunder.

I sift the snow on the mountains below,
    And their great pines groan aghast;
And all the night 'tis my pillow white,
    While I sleep in the arms of the blast.
Sublime on the towers of my skyey bowers,
    Lightning my pilot sits;
In a cavern under is fettered the thunder,
    It struggles and howls at fits;

Over earth and ocean, with gentle motion,
    This pilot is guiding me,
Lured by the love of the genii that move
    In the depths of the purple sea;
Over the rills, and the crags, and the hills.
    Over the lakes and the plains,
Wherever he dreams, under mountain or stream,
    The Spirit he loves remains;
And I all the while bask in Heaven's blue smile,
    Whilst he is dissolving in rains.

I am the daughter of Earth and Water,
    And the nursling of the sky;
I pass through the pores of the ocean and shores;

I change, but I cannot die.
For after the rain, when, with never a stain
   The pavilion of Heaven is bare,
And the winds and sunbeams with their convex gleams
   Build up the blue dome of air,
I silently laugh at my own cenotaph,
   And out of the caverns of rain,
Like a child from the womb, like a ghost from the tomb,
   I arise and unbuild it again.

HOPE'S FORECAST

Ethel Romig Fuller

As a water lily only blooms
When rooted deep in slime,
So peace shall flower, white, cool,
On a future hidden pool
From the murky residue
Of an atomic time.

WHAT KIND OF MUSIC?

James Reeves

What kind of music does Tom like best?
   Drums and fifes and the trumpet's bray.
What kind of music does Jenny like?
   A whirling waltz-tune sweet and gay.

What music pleases Elizabeth?
　　She loves a symphony solemn and grand.
What kind of music does Benny like?
　　A roaring, rhythmical ragtime band.

But the kind of music that Mary loves
　　Is any little gay or comical tune,
Played on a fiddle or clarinet
　　That skips like a leafy stream in June.

WHERE MORE IS MEANT

Christopher Morley

Dazzled, how the brown moth flutters
　　(In my fingers prisoned tight)
Ere, through opened sash and shutters,
　　Loosed into the night.

Surely clutched but softly holden
　　(Least of struggling ticklish things)
Let him go . . .
　　　　My hand is golden,
　　Dusty from his wings.

MEASUREMENT

A. M. Sullivan

Stars and atoms have no size,
They only vary in men's eyes.

Men and instruments will blunder
Calculating things of wonder.

A seed is just as huge a world
As any ball the sun has hurled.

Stars are quite as picayune
As any splinter of the moon.

Time is but a vague device;
Space can never be precise;

Stars and atoms have a girth,
Small as zero, ten times Earth.

There is, by God's swift reckoning,
A universe in everything.

71

BY THE FIRE

Elizabeth Coatsworth

Night herons cry
From still lagoons,
And the waves roar
Beyond the dunes.

The northern lights
Flare wildly green,
And blunt moths flap
Against our screen.

But the yellow fire
Stands fair and tall
And sets its pulse
On ceiling and wall.

And the yellow lamp
Sheds a haloed light
In a wide, still pool
Withstanding the night.

And the yellow cat
In the big chair purrs
As though lamp and fire
And night were hers.

WAVES

Mary Britton Miller

The sea is strange —
Always in motion,
In a state of change.
What is a wave
That the wind can take
The waters and make
The shape of a wave —
What is a wave
That it can break
On the shore and then
Return to the sea
To be shaped again
Into a wave?

A BLACKBIRD SUDDENLY

Joseph Auslander

Heaven is in my hand, and I
Touched a heartbeat of the sky,
Hearing a blackbird cry.

Strange, beautiful, unquiet thing,
Lone flute of God, how can you sing
Winter to spring?

You have outdistanced every voice and word,
And given my spirit wings until it stirred
Like you — a bird.

CLOUDS

Jean Jaszi

A cloud only goes
When the wind blows.

When every leaf hangs limp and still,
A cloud can't cross the smallest hill;
A cloud can only go to sleep,
All piled up in a huge white heap.

A cloud only goes
When the wind blows.

TO THE MOON

Percy Bysshe Shelley

Art thou pale for weariness
Of climbing heaven and gazing on the earth,
Wandering companionless
Among the stars that have a different birth?

HOPPITY TOADS

Aileen Fisher

I always feel sorry
for hoppity toads
whose jackets are dusty
and brownish as roads.

I always think maybe
they sigh overmuch
because they look warty
and floppy and such.

But maybe I'm foolish,
for maybe they'd smile
and chuckle, "Why, dearie,
we're only in STYLE."

For maybe being warty
and dusty as roads
is perfectly proper
for hoppity toads,

for floppity,
    ploppity,
        hoppity
            toads.

AUGURIES OF INNOCENCE

William Blake

To see a World in a grain of sand,
And a Heaven in a wild flower,
Hold Infinity in the palm of your hand,
And Eternity in an hour.

THE MOUNTAINS ARE A LONELY FOLK

Hamlin Garland

The mountains they are silent folk,
    They stand afar — alone;
And the clouds that kiss their brows at night
    Hear neither sigh nor groan.
Each bears him in his ordered place
    As soldiers do, and bold and high
They fold their forests round their feet
    And bolster up the sky.

LOST

Carl Sandburg

Desolate and lone
All night long on the lake

Where fog trails and mist creeps,
The whistle of a boat
Calls and cries unendingly,
Like some lost child
In tears and trouble
Hunting the harbor's breast
And the harbor's eyes.

THE FLOWER-FED BUFFALOES

Vachel Lindsay

The flower-fed buffaloes of the spring
In the days of long ago,
Ranged where the locomotives sing
And the prairie flowers lie low: —
The tossing, blooming, perfumed grass
Is swept away by the wheat,
Wheels and wheels and wheels spin by
In the spring that still is sweet.
But the flower-fed buffaloes of the spring
Let us, long ago.
They gore no more, they bellow no more,
They trundle around the hills no more: —
With the Blackfeet, lying low.
With the Pawnees, lying low,
Lying low.

THE ERIE CANAL

Unknown

I've got a mule, her name is Sal,
Fifteen miles on the Erie Canal.
She's a good old worker and a good old pal,
Fifteen miles on the Erie Canal.
We've haul'd some barges in our day,
Fill'd with lumber, coal and hay,
And we know ev'ry inch of the way
From Albany to Buffalo.

Refrain
Low bridge, ev'rybody down!
Low bridge, for we're going through a town,
And you'll always know your neighbor,
You'll always know your pal,
If you ever navigated on the Erie Canal.

We better get along on our way, old gal,
Fifteen miles on the Erie Canal,
Cause you bet your life I'd never part with Sal,
Fifteen miles on the Erie Canal.

Git up there, mule, here comes a lock,
We'll make Rome 'bout six o'clock,
One more trip and back we'll go
Right back home to Buffalo.

NIGHT HERDING SONG

Harry Stephens

Oh, slow up, dogies, quit your roving round,
You have wandered and tramped all over the ground;
Oh, graze along, dogies, and feed kinda slow,
And don't be forever on the go, —
Oh, move slow, dogies, move slow.

I have circle-herded, trail-herded, night-herded,
   and cross-herded, too,
But to keep you together that's what I can't do;
My horse is leg-weary and I'm awful tired,
But if you get away I'm sure to get fired, —
Bunch up, little dogies, bunch up.

Oh, say, little dogies, when are goin' to lay down,
And quit this forever shiftin' around?
My limbs are weary, my seat is sore;
Oh, lay down, dogies, like you've laid down before, —
Lay down, little dogies, lay down.

Oh, lay still, dogies, since you have laid down,
Stretch away out on the big open ground;
Snore loud, little dogies, and drown the wild sound
That will go away when the day rolls round, —
Lay still, little dogies, lay still.

CORN-GRINDING SONG

Trans. by Natalie Curtis

Yonder, yonder see the fair rainbow,
See the rainbow brightly decked and painted!
Now the swallow bringeth glad news to your corn,
Singing "Hitherward, hitherward, hitherward, rain,
   Hither, come!"
Singing, "Hitherward, hitherward, hitherward, white cloud,
   Hither, come!"
Now hear the corn-plants murmur,
"We are growing everywhere!
Hi, yai! The world, how fair!"

OREAD

H. D.

Whirl up, sea —
whirl your pointed pines,
splash your great pines
on our rocks,
hurl your green over us,
cover us with your pools of fir.

80

A VIOLET BANK

William Shakespeare

I know a bank whereon the wild thyme blows,
Where oxlips and the nodding violet grow;
Quite over-canopied with lush woodbine,
With sweet musk roses and with eglantine.

SEA SHELL

Amy Lowell

Sea Shell, Sea Shell,
   Sing me a song, O please!
A Song of ships, and sailormen,
   And parrots, and tropical trees,

Of islands lost in the Spanish Main
Which no man ever may find again,
Of fishes and corals under the waves,
And sea horses stabled in great green caves.

Sea Shell, Sea Shell,
Sing of the things you know so well.

WIND-SONG

Trans. by Natalie Curtis

Far on the desert ridges
Stands the cactus;
Lo, the blossoms swaying
To and fro, the blossoms swaying, swaying.

THE LOCUST

Trans. by Frank Cushing

Locust, locust, playing a flute,
Locust, locust, playing a flute!
Away up above on the pine-tree bough,
Closely clinging,
Playing a flute,
Playing a flute!

SPLINTER

Carl Sandburg

The voice of the last cricket
across the first frost
is one kind of good-by.
It is so thin a splinter of singing.

PHOSPHORESCENCE

Melville Cane

       Fireflies
       Play hide-and-seek in the tall grass,
       Rise and improvise
       Their lacy traceries,
       Flitter,
       Circle,
       Glitter,
       Pass and loop and counterpass,
       Twinkle,
       Darkle,
       Sprinkle
       Sparkles.

GOLDENHAIR

James Joyce

       Lean out of the window,
         Goldenhair;
       I hear you singing
         A merry air.

       My book was closed;
         I read no more,
       Watching the fire dance
         On the floor.

I have left my book,
   I have left my room,
For I heard you singing
   Through the gloom.

Singing and singing
   A merry air,
Lean out of the window,
   Goldenhair.

DETAILS

Luke Zilles

Let things touch your mind
the same way one raindrop hits
the pane just before
it begins to rain,
and the dust of the glass is
streaked with one clean line.

Let things touch your mind
lightly as the grasshopper
leaps from a stalk of
grass, and the stalk springs
up with the ripple, the thrill
of the thing it knew.

THE WANDERING MOON

James Reeves

Age after age and all alone,
 She turns through endless space,
Showing the watchers on the earth
 Her round and rocky face.
Enchantment comes upon all hearts
 That feel her lonely grace.

Mount Newton is the highest peak
 Upon the wandering moon,
And there perhaps the witches dance
 To some fantastic tune,
And in the half-light cold and grey
 Their incantations croon.

And there perhaps mad creatures come
 To play at hide-and-seek
With howling apes and blundering bears
 And bats that swoop and squeak.
I cannot see what nameless things
 Go on at Newton Peak.

I cannot tell what vessels move
 Across the Nubian Sea,
Nor whether any bird alights
 On any stony tree.

A quarter of a million miles
   Divide the moon and me.

A quarter of a million miles —
   It is a fearsome way,
But ah! if we could only fly
   On some auspicious day
And land at last on Newton Peak,
   Ah then, what games we'd play!

What songs we'd sing on Newton Peak,
   On what wild journeys go
By frozen fen or burning waste,
   Or where the moon-flowers grow,
And countless strange and fearful things —
   If only we could know!

BUNCH OF WILD FLOWERS

Luke Zilles

There's no arrangement. It is a thicket in little
of the nondescript, the riffraff of the field,
as miscellaneous here as where you found them growing.
In the glass jar of water they look much
as when you broke them and carried them home in your
   hand.

Some would say, "Weeds." They have the look of trash.
But this is simply the character of where they grew,
an asperity about them, stiff in spike,
stalk, leaf, and natively savage in purple
loosestrife, orange milkweed, and goldenrod.

What you brought back to stick in water is the field,
a part of the tangle and tramp of the afternoon.
They are the pollen and dust on your shoes, grasshoppers
before you, the straw of summer wilderness,
the burn in your face, and still, the sun in your eyes.

THE SEA BIRD TO THE WAVE

Padraic Colum

> On and on,
> O white brother!
> Thunder does not daunt thee!
> How thou movest!
> By thine impulse —
> With no wing!
> Fairest thing
> The wide sea shows me!
> On and on,
> O white brother!
>
> Art thou gone?

NIGHT CLOUDS

Amy Lowell

The white mares of the moon rush along the sky
Beating their golden hoofs upon the glass heavens;
The white mares of the moon are all standing on their hind
   legs
Pawing at the green porcelain doors of the remote heavens.
Fly, mares!
Strain your utmost,
Scatter the milky dust of stars,
Or the tiger sun will leap upon you and destroy you
With one lick of his vermilion tongue.

EVERYONE SANG

Siegfried Sassoon

Everyone suddenly burst out singing;
And I was fill'd with such delight
As prison'd birds must find in freedom
Winging wildly across the white
Orchards and dark green fields; on; on; and out of sight.

Everyone's voice was suddenly lifted,
And beauty came like the setting sun.
My heart was shaken with tears; and horror

Drifted away . . . O but every one
Was a bird; and the song was wordless; the singing will
  never be done.

SHE WALKS IN BEAUTY

Lord Byron

　　She walks in beauty, like the night
　　　　Of cloudless climes and starry skies;
　　And all that's best of dark and bright
　　　　Meet in her aspect and her eyes;
　　Thus mellowed to that tender light
　　　　Which heaven to gaudy day denies.

　　One shade the more, one ray the less
　　　　Had half impair'd the nameless grace,
　　Which waves in every raven tress,
　　　　Or softly lightens o'er her face;
　　Where thoughts severely sweet express
　　　　How pure, how dear, their dwelling-place.

　　And on that cheek, and o'er that brow,
　　　　So soft, so calm, yet eloquent,
　　The smiles that win, the tints that glow,
　　　　But tell of days in goodness spent,
　　A mind at peace with all below,
　　　　A heart whose love is innocent.

Private
Worlds

PSALM 23

The Bible

The Lord is my shepherd; I shall not want.
He maketh me to lie down in green pastures:
he leadeth me beside the still waters.
He restoreth my soul: he leadeth me in the
paths of righteousness for his name's sake.
Yea, though I walk through the valley of
the shadow of death, I will fear no evil:
for thou art with me; thy rod and thy staff
they comfort me.
Thou preparest a table before me in the
presence of mine enemies: thou anointest
my head with oil; my cup runneth over.
Surely goodness and mercy shall follow
me all the days of my life: and I will
dwell in the house of the Lord for ever.

PSALM 100

The Bible

Make a joyful noise unto the Lord, all ye lands.
Serve the Lord with gladness: come before his
presence with singing.
Know ye that the Lord he is God: it is he that
hath made us, and not we ourselves; we are his

people, and the sheep of the pasture.
Enter into his gates with thanksgiving, and into
his courts with praise: be thankful unto him,
and bless his name.
For the Lord is good; his mercy is everlasting;
and his truth endureth to all generations.

TRY AGAIN

William Edward Hickson

'Tis a lesson you should heed,
　　　Try again;
If at first you don't succeed,
　　　Try again;
Then your courage should appear,
For if you will persevere,
You will conquer, never fear,
　　　Try again.

Once or twice though you should fail,
　　　Try again;
If you would at last prevail,
　　　Try again;
If we strive, 'tis no disgrace
Though we do not win the race.
What should we do in that case?
　　　Try again.

If you find your task is hard,
        Try again;
Time will bring you your reward,
        Try again;
All that other folk can do,
Why, with patience, may not you?
Only keep this rule in view,
        Try again.

from TREASURY OF VERSE
FOR LITTLE CHILDREN.
Compiled by M. G. Edgar
(1936). Thomas Y. Crowell
Company, Publishers

THIS MOMENT YEARNING
AND THOUGHTFUL

Walt Whitman

This moment yearning and thoughtful sitting alone,
It seems to me there are other men in other lands yearning
    and thoughtful,
It seems to me I can look over and behold them in Germany,
    Italy, France, Spain,
Or far, far away, in China, or in Russia or Japan, talking
    other dialects,
And it seems to me if I could know those other men I should
    become attached to them as I do to men in my own lands,
O I know we should be brethren and lovers,
I know I should be happy with them.

94

A GREEN PLACE

William Jay Smith

I know a place all fennel-green and fine
Far from the white icecap, the glacial flaw,
Where shy mud hen and dainty porcupine
Dance in delight by a quivering pawpaw;

Dance by catalpa tree and flowering peach
With speckled guinea fowl and small raccoon,
While the heron, from his perforated beach,
Extends one bony leg beyond the moon.

I know a place so green and fennel-fine
Its boundary is air; and will you come?
A bellflower tinkles by a trumpet vine,
A shrouded cricket taps a midget drum.

There blue flies buzz among the wild sweet peas;
The water speaks: black insects pluck the stream.
May-apples cluster there by bearded trees,
Full-skirted dancers risen from a dream.

Birds call; twigs crackle; wild marsh grasses sway;
Will you come soon, before the cold winds blow
To swirl the dust and drive the leaves away,
And thin-ribbed earth pokes out against the snow?

MENDING WALL

Robert Frost

Something there is that doesn't love a wall,
That sends the frozen-ground-swell under it,
And spills the upper boulders in the sun;
And makes gaps even two can pass abreast.
The work of hunters is another thing:
I have come after them and made repair
Where they have left not one stone on a stone,
But they would have the rabbit out of hiding,
To please the yelping dogs. The gaps I mean,
No one has seen them made or heard them made,
But at spring mending-time we find them there.
I let my neighbor know beyond the hill;
And on a day we meet to walk the line
And set the wall between us as we go.
To each the boulders that have fallen to each.
And some are loaves and some so nearly balls
We have to use a spell to make them balance:
'Stay where you are until our backs are turned!'
We wear our fingers rough with handling them.
Oh, just another kind of outdoor game,
One on a side. It comes to little more:
There where it is we do not need the wall:
He is all pine and I am apple-orchard.
My apple trees will never get across
And eat the cones under his pines, I tell him
He only says, 'Good fences make good neighbors.'
Spring is the mischief in me, and I wonder

If I could put a notion in his head;
'*Why* do they make good neighbors? Isn't it
Where there are cows? But here there are no cows.
Before I built a wall I'd ask to know
What I was walling in or walling out,
And to whom I was like to give offence.
Something there is that doesn't love a wall,
That wants it down! I could say 'Elves' to him,
But it's not elves exactly, and I'd rather
He said it for himself. I see him there
Bringing a stone grasped firmly by the top
In each hand, like an old-stone savage armed.
He moves in darkness as it seems to me,
Not of woods only and the shade of trees.
He will not go behind his father's saying,
And he likes having thought of it so well
He says again, 'Good fences make good neighbors.'

ANDRE

Gwendolyn Brooks

I had a dream last night, I dreamed
I had to pick a Mother out.
I had to choose a Father too.
At first, I wondered what to do,
There were so many there, it seemed,
Short and tall and thin and stout.

But just before I sprang awake,
I knew what parents I would take.

And *this* surprised and made me glad:
They were the ones I always had!

WINTER BRANCHES

Margaret Widdemer

When winter-time grows wearying, I lift my eyes on high
And see the black trees standing there, stripped clear against
the sky;
They stand there very silent, with the cold flushed sky behind,
The little twigs flare beautiful and restful and kind,

Clearcut and certain now they rise, with summer past,
For all that trees can ever learn they know now, at last:

Still and black and wonderful, with all unrest gone by,
The stripped tree-boughs comfort me, drawn clear against the
sky.

RUDOLPH IS TIRED OF THE CITY

Gwendolyn Brooks

These buildings are too close to me.
I'd like to PUSH away.
I'd like to live in the country,
And spread my arms all day.

I'd like to spread my breath out, too —
As farmers' sons and daughters do.

I'd tend the cows and chickens.
I'd do the other chores.
Then, all the hours left I'd go
A-SPREADING out-of-doors.

TRAVEL

Edna St. Vincent Millay

The railroad track is miles away,
    And the day is loud with voices speaking,
Yet there isn't a train goes by all day
    But I hear its whistle shrieking.

All night there isn't a train goes by
   Though the night is still for sleep and dreaming,
But I see its cinders red on the sky,
   And I hear its engine steaming.

My heart is warm with the friends I make,
   And better friends I'll not be knowing,
Yet there isn't a train I wouldn't take,
   No matter where it's going.

HILLS

Arthur Guiterman

I never loved your plains! —
   Your gentle valleys,
Your drowsy country lanes
   And pleached alleys.

I want my hills! — the trail
   That scorns the hollow.
Up, up the ragged shale
   Where few will follow.

Up, over wooded crest
   And mossy boulder
With strong thigh, heaving chest,
   And swinging shoulder.

100

So let me hold my way,
　By nothing halted,
Until, at close of day,
　I stand, exalted.

High on my hills of dream —
　Dear hills that know me!
And then, how fair will seem
　The lands below me.

How pure, at vesper-time,
　The far bells chiming!
God, give me hills to climb,
　And strength for climbing.

HE ATE AND DRANK THE PRECIOUS WORDS

Emily Dickinson

He ate and drank the precious words
His spirit grew robust;
He knew no more that he was poor,
Nor that his frame was dust.
He danced along the dingy days,
And this bequest of wings
Was but a book. What liberty
A loosened spirit brings!

THE UNEXPLORER

Edna St. Vincent Millay

There was a road ran past our house
Too lovely to explore.
I asked my mother once — she said
That if you followed where it led
It brought you to a milkman's door.
(That's why I have not traveled more.)

RULES FOR THE ROAD

Edwin Markham

Stand straight:
Step firmly, throw your weight:
Then heaven is high above your head,
The good gray road is faithful to your tread.

Be strong:
Sing to your heart a battle song:
Though hidden foemen lie in wait,
Something is in you that can smile at fate.

Press through:
Nothing can harm you if you are true.
And when the night comes, rest:
The earth is friendly as a mother's breast.

A SONG OF GREATNESS

Transcribed by Mary Austin

A CHIPPEWA INDIAN SONG
When I hear the old men
Telling of heroes,
Telling of great deeds
Of ancient days,
When I hear them telling,
Then I think within me
I too am one of these.

When I hear the people
Praising great ones,
Then I know that I too
Shall be esteemed,
I too when my time comes
Shall do mightily.

GOD'S WORLD

Edna St. Vincent Millay

O world, I cannot hold thee close enough!
Thy winds, thy wide grey skies!
Thy mists, that roll and rise!

Thy woods, this autumn day, that ache and sag
And all but cry with colour! That gaunt crag
To crush! To lift the lean of that black buff!
World, World, I cannot get thee close enough!

Long have I known a glory in it all,
   But never knew I this:
   Here such a passion is
As stretcheth me apart, — Lord, I do fear
Thou'st made the world too beautiful this year;
My soul is all but out of me, — let fall
No burning leaf; prithee, let no bird call.

SPRING

Richard Hovey

I said in my heart, "I am sick of four walls and a ceiling.
I have need of the sky.
I have business with the grass.
I will up and get me away where the hawk is wheeling,
Lone and high,
And the snow clouds go by . . ."

ECHOES

Walter de la Mare

> The sea laments
> The livelong day,
> Fringing its waste of sand;
> Cries back from the whispering shore —
> No words I understand.
>
> Yet it echoes in my heart a voice,
> As far, as near, as these —
> The wind that weeps,
> The solemn surge
> Of strange and lonely seas.

THE GRASS SO LITTLE HAS TO DO

Emily Dickinson

> The grass so little has to do, —
> A sphere of simple green,
> With only butterflies to brood,
> And bees to entertain,
>
> And stir all day to pretty tunes
> The breezes fetch along,
> And hold the sunshine in its lap
> And bow to everything;

And thread the dews all night, like pearls,
And make itself so fine, —
A duchess were too common
For such a noticing.

And even when it dies, to pass
In odors so divine,
As lowly spices gone to sleep,
Or amulets of pine.

And then to dwell in sovereign barns,
And dream the days away, —
The grass so little has to do,
I wish I were a hay!

I CAN CLIMB OUR APPLE TREE

Jessie Orton Jones

I can climb our apple tree,
If I put my feet carefully in the right places,
    And pull myself up by my hands.
Then I come to my little seat in the arms of the tree.
    I can sit there and see everything.
I can see a measuring worm, light green,
    Climbing our apple tree.
    At every step
He has to make his whole body into a hump,
While his back feet catch up with his front feet.

That is a hard way to climb a tree,
But it's his way
And he doesn't seem to mind.

MAKE BELIEVE

Harry Behn

I made believe fly
A bird so blue
It glowed like sky —
And up it flew!

I made believe grow
A tree in the wood
With petals of snow —
And there it stood!

I'd love to pretend
A dragon for fun,
But if in the end
I saw it — I'd run!

So I'll make up a very
Small elf instead
To sing in the moonlight
Beside my bed.

THE COIN

Sara Teasdale

Into my heart's treasury
I slipped a coin
That time cannot take
Nor a thief purloin, —
Oh, better than the minting
Of a gold-crowned king
Is the safe-kept memory
Of a lovely thing.

CITY TREES

Edna St. Vincent Millay

The trees along this city street,
Save for the traffic and the trains,
Would make a sound as thin and sweet
As trees in country lanes.

And people standing in their shade
Out of a shower, undoubtedly
Would hear such music as is made
Upon a country tree.

Oh, little leaves that are so dumb
   Against the shrieking city air,
I watch you when the wind has come, —
   I know what sound is there.

I WANT A PASTURE

Rachel Field

I want a pasture for next door neighbor;
   The sea to be just across the way.
I want to stand at my door for hours
   Talking and passing the time of day
Unhurried, as country people do
   Season on season, a whole year through.

I want to give greeting to frost and sun;
   To gossip with thunder and tides and bees;
To mark the doings of wind in boughs;
   Watch apples redden on crooked trees.
I want to hail each passing thing
   That moves, fleet-footed, by fin, or wing.

I want far islands to grow familiar
   As neighbors' faces; clouds be more plain
Than granite boulder; than web of spider
   Patterned with intricate drops of rain.
I want to be wise as the oldest star,
   Young as the waves and grasses are.

THE SECRET CAVERN

Margaret Widdemer

Underneath the boardwalk, way, way back,
There's a splendid cavern, big and black —
If you want to get there, you must crawl
Underneath the posts and steps and all
When I've finished paddling, there I go —
None of all the other children know!

There I keep my treasures in a box —
Shells and colored glass and queer-shaped rocks,
In a secret hiding place I've made,
Hollowed out with clamshells and a spade,
Marked with yellow pebbles in a row —
None of all the other children know!

It's a place that makes a splendid lair,
Room for chests and weapons and one chair.
In the farthest corner, by the stones,
I shall have a flag with skulls and bones
And a lamp that casts a lurid glow —
None of all the other children know!

Sometime, by and by, when I am grown,
I shall go and live there all alone;
I shall dig and paddle till it's dark,
Then go out and man my private bark:
I shall fill my cave with captive foe —
None of all the other children know!

THE ELEMENTS

William H. Davies

No house of stone
  Was built for me;
When the Sun shines —
  I am a bee.

No sooner comes
  The Rain so warm,
I come to light —
  I am a worm.

When the Winds blow,
  I do not strip,
But set my sails —
  I am a ship.

When Lightning comes,
  It plays with me
And I with it —
  I am a tree.

When drowned men rise
  At Thunder's word,
Sings Nightingale —
  I am a bird.

DAYS

Karle Wilson Baker

Some days my thoughts are just cocoons — all cold, and dull, and blind,
They hang from dripping branches in the grey woods of my mind;

And other days they drift and shine — such free and flying things!
I find the gold-dust in my hair, left by their brushing wings.

INDIANS

John Fandel

Margaret mentioned Indians,
And I began to think about Indians —

Indians once living
Where now we are living —

And I thought how little I know
About Indians. Oh, I know

What I have heard. Not much,
When I think how much

I wonder about them,
When a mere mention of them,

INDIANS, starts me. I
Think of their wigwams. I

Think of canoes. I think
Of quick arrows. I think

Of things Indian. And still
I think of their bright, still

Summers, when these hills
And meadows on these hills

Shone in the morning
Suns before this morning.

ESCAPE

Elinor Wylie

When foxes eat the last gold grape,
And the last white antelope is killed,
I shall stop fighting and escape
Into a little house I'll build.

But first I'll shrink to fairy size,
With a whisper no one understands,
Making blind moons of all your eyes,
And muddy roads of all your hands.

And may you grope for me in vain
In hollows under the mangrove root,
Or where, in apple-scented rain,
The silver wasp-nests hang like fruit.

MY WISH

Patience Strong

When the moon comes peeping through my windowpane at
  night,
I wish I had it on a string, that ball of silver light,

To fly it like a kite above the houses in the Square,
Wouldn't it be fun to see the people stop and stare.

One gets tired of snakes-and-ladders, tricycles and tops,
Hunting robbers in the woods and munching acid drops,
This is what I keep on wishing. More than anything,
I'd like to walk to London with the moon upon a string.

PICTURES IN THE FIRE

Patience Strong

What do you see in the fire tonight?
I see the oddest things:
A castle on a mountain-top
A bird with flaming wings.
An old old man, a gnome I think,
A dwarf with pointed beard,
A cottage with three chimney pots.
A forest, wild and weird.
I see a ruby-studded cave,
With crimson stalactites.
And just behind that bit of coal
There are the strangest sights.
A lady with a basket
And a small boy with a dog.
Can't you see them seated there
Upon the apple log?

LODGED

Robert Frost

The rain to the wind said,
'You push and I'll pelt.'
They so smote the garden bed
That the flowers actually knelt,
And lay lodged — though not dead.
I know how the flowers felt.

A VAGABOND SONG

Bliss Carman

There is something in the autumn that is native to my
blood —
Touch of manner, hint of mood;
And my heart is like a rhyme,
With the yellow and the purple and the crimson keeping time.

The scarlet of the maples can shake me like a cry
Of bugles going by.
And my lonely spirit thrills
To see the frosty asters like a smoke upon the hills.

There is something in October sets the gypsy blood astir;
We must rise and follow her,
When from every hill of flame
She calls and calls each vagabond by name.

LEISURE

William H. Davies

What is this life if, full of care,
We have no time to stand and stare?

No time to stand beneath the boughs
And stare as long as sheep or cows.

No time to see, when woods we pass,
Where squirrels hide their nuts in grass.

No time to see, in broad daylight,
Streams full of stars, like skies at night.

No time to turn at Beauty's glance,
And watch her feet, how they can dance.

No time to wait till her mouth can
Enrich that smile her eyes began.

A poor life this if, full of care.
We have not time to stand and stare.

Merry Moments

FATHER WILLIAM

Lewis Carroll

"You are old, Father William," the young man said,
   "And your hair has become very white;
And yet you incessantly stand on your head —
   Do you think at your age, it is right?"

"In my youth," Father William replied to his son,
   "I feared it might injure the brain;
But, now that I'm perfectly sure I have none,
   Why, I do it again and again."

"You are old," said the youth, "as I mentioned before.
   And have grown most uncommonly fat;
Yet you turned a back-somersault in at the door —
   Pray, what is the reason of that?"

"In my youth," said the sage, as he shook his grey locks,
   "I kept all my limbs very supple
By the use of this ointment — one shilling the box —
   Allow me to sell you a couple?"

"You are old," said the youth, "and your jaws are too weak
   For anything tougher than suet;
Yet you finished the goose, with the bones and the beak —
   Pray, how did you manage to do it?"

"In my youth," said his father, "I took to the law,
  And argued each case with my wife;
And the muscular strength which it gave to my jaw
  Has lasted the rest of my life."

"You are old," said the youth, "one would hardly suppose
  That your eye was as steady as ever;
Yet you balanced an eel on the end of your nose —
  What made you so awfully clever?"

"I have answered three questions, and that is enough,"
  Said his father. "Don't give yourself airs!
Do you think I can listen all day to such stuff?
  Be off, or I'll kick you downstairs!"

THE SNIFFLE

Ogden Nash

      In spite of her sniffle,
      Isabel's chiffle.
      Some girls with a sniffle
      Would be weepy and tiffle;
      They would look awful,
      Like a rained-on waffle,
      But Isabel's chiffle
      In spite of her sniffle.
      Her nose is more red
      With a cold in her head,

121

But then, to be sure,
Her eyes are bluer.
Some girls with a snuffle,
Their tempers are uffle,
But when Isabel's snivelly
She's snivelly civilly,
And when she is snuffly
She's perfectly luffly.

THE FABLE OF THE MAGNET
AND THE CHURN

W. S. Gilbert

A magnet hung in a hardware shop,
And all around was a loving crop
Of scissors and needles, nails and knives,
Offering love for all their lives;
But for iron the magnet felt no whim,
Though he charmed iron, it charmed not him;
From needles and nails and knives he'd turn,
For he'd set his love on a Silver Churn!

His most aesthetic,
Very magnetic
Fancy took this turn —
"If I can wheedle
A knife or a needle,
Why not a Silver Churn?"

And Iron and Steel expressed surprise,
The needles opened their well-drilled eyes,
The penknives felt "shut up," no doubt,
The scissors declared themselves "cut out,"
The kettles boiled with rage, 'tis said,
While every nail went off its head,
And hither and thither began to roam,
Till a hammer came up — and drove them home.

While this magnetic,
Peripatetic
Lover he lived to learn,
By no endeavor
Can a magnet ever
Attract a Silver Churn!

A NAUTICAL BALLAD

Charles Edward Carryl

A capital ship for an ocean trip,
    Was the Walloping Window-Blind.
No gale that blew dismayed her crew,
    Nor troubled the captain's mind.

The man at the wheel was taught to feel
    Contempt for the wildest blow;
And it often appeared — when the weather had cleared —
    He had been in his bunk below.

The boatswain's mate was very sedate,
    Yet fond of amusement, too;
And he played hopscotch with the starboard watch,
    While the captain tickled the crew.

And the gunner we had was apparently mad,
    For he sat on the after-rail
And fired salutes with the captain's boots
    In the teeth of the booming gale.

The captain sat on the commodore's hat,
    And dined in a royal way,
Off toasted pigs and pickles and figs
    And gunnery bread each day.

The cook was Dutch and behaved as such,
    For the diet he gave the crew,
Was a number of tons of hot-cross buns,
    Served up with sugar and glue.

All nautical pride we laid aside,
    And we cast our vessel ashore,
On the Gulliby Isles, where the Poo-Poo smiles
    And the Rumpletum-Bunders roar.

We sat on the edge of a sandy ledge,
    And shot at the whistling bee:
And the cinnamon bats wore waterproof hats,
    As they danced by the sounding sea.

On Rug-gub bark, from dawn till dark,
    We fed, till we had all grown
Uncommonly shrunk; when a Chinese junk
    Came in from the Torriby Zone.

She was stubby and square, but we didn't much care,
    So we cheerily put to sea;
And we left the crew of the junk to chew
    The bark of the Rug-gub tree.

A TRACT FOR AUTOS

Arthur Guiterman

Come, all you little Runabouts
    And gather round my Knee;
I'll tell you of a Touring Car
    As bad as bad could be:

It worked its Klaxon overtime
    To make a Horrid Noise
And thought it Fun to muss up Hens
    and little Girls and Boys.

It used to blow its Tires out
    To hear its Owner swear,
And loved to balk on Trolley Tracks
    To give his Friends a Scare.

At last this naughty Touring Car
　　Got drunk on Too Much Oil,
And went a-boiling up the Road
　　As hard as it could boil;

And went a-plunging, tumbling down
　　A dreadful, dark Ravine;
And there it burns and burns and burns
　　In smelly Gasoline!

Another little Touring Car
　　Was very, very good;
It always minded Brake and Wheel,
　　And never splashed its Hood.

It wouldn't skid, nor anger Folks
　　By giving them a Shove,
But cooed as gently through its Horn
　　As any Sucking Dove.

It never grew Unmannerly
　　To Market-Cart or Dray,
But whispered, "Please," and "Thank you, Sir!"
　　To those that blocked its Way.

It never scattered Bolts and Plugs
　　About the Countryside
But did its Level Best to be
　　Its Owner's Joy and Pride.

So, when 'twas Time to yield its Place
　To Models fresh and new,
This lively little Touring Car
　Developed Planes and flew!

EIGHT LIMERICKS

Edward Lear

1

There was an Old Man in a tree,
Who was horribly bored by a bee;
　When they said, 'Does it buzz?'
　He replied, 'Yes it does!
It's a regular brute of a bee!'

2

There was an Old Person of Hurst,
Who drank when he was not athirst;
　When they said, 'You'll grow fatter!'
　He answered, 'What matter?'
That globular Person of Hurst.

3

There was a Young Lady whose nose,
Was so long that it reached to her toes;
　So she hired an old lady,
　Whose conduct was steady,
To carry that wonderful nose.

4

There was an Old Man of Corfu
Who never knew what he should do;
　　So he rushed up and down
　　Till the sun made him brown,
That bewildered Old Man of Corfu.

5

There was an Old Man of the Dee,
Who was sadly annoyed by a flea;
　　When he said, 'I will scratch it,'
　　They gave him a hatchet,
Which grieved that Old Man of the Dee.

6

There was an Old Person of Minety,
Who purchased five-hundred and ninety
　　Large apples and pears,
　　Which he threw unawares,
At the heads of the people of Minety.

7

There was an Old Man of Hong Kong,
Who never did anything wrong;
　　He lay on his back,
　　With his head in a sack,
That innocuous Old Man of Hong Kong.

8

There was an Old Person of Ware,
Who rode on the back of a Bear;
   When they ask'd, 'Does it trot?' —
   He said, 'Certainly not!
He's a Moppsikon Floppsikon Bear!'

POCKETS

Rowena Bennett

I never knew a kangaroo —
   A sister or a brother —
Who didn't ride, when young, inside
   The pocket of his mother;
And, oh, I'm sure that kangaroos
   Think human folk are funny
To fill their pockets up with things
   As valueless as money.

A BOWL OF OCTOBER

Helen Bevington

October is a breakfast food
With fields of shredded wheat.
The golden cornflakes lie on the lawn,
And wheaties lie in the street.

The puffed rice clouds, the grapenut hills,
Oh! the oatmeal skies, abed
Have wakened me in the crispies air —
And so I have breakfasted.

DR. FELL AND POINTS WEST

Ogden Nash

Your train leaves at eleven forty-five and it is now but eleven
    thirty-nine and a half,
And there is only one man ahead of you at the ticket window
    so you have plenty of time, haven't you, well I hope you
    enjoy a hearty laugh,
Because he is Dr. Fell, and he is engaged in an intricate
    maneuver,
He wants to go to Sioux City with stopovers at Plymouth
    Rock, Stone Mountain, Yellowstone Park, Lake Louise
    and Vancouver,
And he would like some information about an alternate
    route,
One that would include New Orleans and Detroit, with pos-
    sibly a day or two in Minneapolis and Butte,
And when the agent has compiled the data with the aid of a
    slug of aromatic spirits and a moist bandanna,
He says that settles it, he'll spend his vacation canoeing up
    and down the Susquehanna,
And oh yes, which way is the bus terminal and what's play-
    ing at the Rivoli,

And how do the railroads expect to stay in business when
their employees are incapable of answering a simple question accurately or civilly?

He then demands and receives change for twenty dollars and
saunters off leaving everybody's jaw with a sag on it,

And when you finally get to buy your ticket not only has
your train gone but you also discover that your porter has
efficiently managed to get your bag on it.

CLOTHES

Frances Frost

The rabbit thieves in silver suit;
The muskrat dives in brown;
But I, who grow no covering,
Must scurry through the town
In summer, winter,
Fall, and spring,
To find my seasonal
Garmenting.

I envy woodchuck,
Fox, and mink,
Who never have
To stop and think
About their clothes, but trot the world
In fitted coats and proud,
Nor have to change to nibble buds
Or take a drink of cloud.

131

IN PRAISE OF DUST

Rachel Field

> Dust is such a pleasant thing —
> A soft gray kind of covering
> For furniture, whereon to draw
> Letters and pictures by the score.
> Why won't the grown-ups let dust stay,
> Instead of brushing it away?

NECKS

Rowena Bennett

> The swan has a neck that is curly and long.
> The camel has one that is shaggy and strong.
> But the spotted giraffe
> Has a neck and a half.

FIGHT

Jean Jaszi

> Cat and I
> We had a fight;
> I hit,
> Cat bit,
> We quit.

THE TALE OF THE SKUNK AND POOR JEZ

John Becker

Jezebel Jones smelled really punk
From having tried to catch a skunk.
Her sister Sue, the little brat,
Had told the child it was a cat —
And so it was.

Some cats are white and some are blue
And quite a few are tiger too;
Some cats are Toms and some are not,
Some are neuter, some are pewter;
Some howl at night, all prowl at night,
Some are Persian, some Angora,
China, Cheshire, Glanamora;
Some are manx and some are lynx,
And one's a sphinx.

The lion lords it o'er them all,
Over the short and over the tall.
But he's no pet. To catch a cat
You catch him small. But sister Sue
Did not tell Jez what I tell you:
Only the pole-cat is a skunk
And that's why Jezebel smelled so punk.

SNAIL

David McCord

This sticky trail
Was made by snail.
Snail makes no track
That he'll take back.
However slow,
His word is go.
(Twixt me and you
The word is goo.)

PICK ME UP

William Jay Smith

Pick me up with a pile of blocks
And carry me past the Cuckoo Clocks!

Pick me up with a pile of hay
And carry me off to Buzzards Bay!

Pick me up with a pile of snow
And carry me out to Idaho!

Pick me up with a pile of twine
And carry me down to the Argentine!

Pick me up with a pile of lava
And carry me over the hills of Java!

Pick me up with a pile of sand
And put me down in New Foundland!

TOM DUCKET

Jean Jaszi

Tom Ducket, Tom Ducket,
Fell in a bucket,
Couldn't get up to get out;
He was stucket.

THE PANDA

William Jay Smith

A lady who lived in Uganda
Was outrageously fond of her Panda:
With her Chinchilla Cat,
It ate grasshopper fat
On an air-conditioned veranda.

135

OF ALL THE IDIOTS THAT ABOUND

Samuel Hoffenstein

Of all the idiots that abound
Above, beneath, and on the ground,
The blinking squirrel is to me
The deepest-sunk in idiocy —
He builds himself a catacomb
Among the worms, and calls it home,
And there he cowers, sore afraid
Of bird and beast and man and maid,
And when, at last, he leaves his rut,
His goal is just another nut.

THE LION

Vachel Lindsay

The Lion is a kingly beast.
He likes a Hindu for a feast.
And if no Hindu he can get,
The lion-family is upset.

He cuffs his wife and bites her ears
Till she is nearly moved to tears.
Then some explorer finds the den
And all is family peace again.

THE EMBARRASSING EPISODE OF LITTLE MISS MUFFET

Guy Wetmore Carryl

Little Miss Muffet discovered a tuffet,
  (Which never occurred to the rest of us)
And, as 'twas a June day, and just about noonday,
  She wanted to eat — like the best of us;
Her diet was whey, and I hasten to say
  It is wholesome and people grow fat on it.
The spot being lonely, the lady not only
  Discovered the tuffet, but sat on it.

A rivulet gabbled beside her and babbled,
  As rivulets always are thought to do,
And dragon flies sported around and cavorted,
  As poets say dragon flies ought to do;
When, glancing aside for a moment, she spied
  A horrible sight that brought fear to her,
A hideous spider was sitting beside her,
  And most unavoidably near to her!

Albeit unsightly, this creature politely
  Said: "Madam, I earnestly vow to you,
I'm penitent that I did not bring my hat. I
  Should otherwise certainly bow to you."
Though anxious to please, he was so ill at ease
  That he lost all his sense of propriety,
And grew so inept that he clumsily stept
  In her plate — which is barred in Society.

This curious error completed her terror;
   She shuddered, and growing much paler, not
Only left her tuffet, but dealt him a buffet
   Which doubled him up in a sailor knot.
It should be explained that at this he was pained:
   He cried: "I have vexed you, no doubt of it!
Your fist's like a truncheon." "You're still in my luncheon,"
   Was all that she answered. "Get out of it!"

And the MORAL is this: Be it madam or miss
   To whom you have something to say,
You are only absurd when you get in the curd,
   But you're rude when you get in the whey!

A LUCKY THING

Dorothy Aldis

A Snap-Dragon will never snap
He's only wild in name.
Standing in a garden bed
The poor thing's very tame.

Nor does a Dande-Lion Roar
Which is a lucky thing:
With all the millions that there are
That would be frightening.

138

SAINT GEORGE AND THE DRAGON

Alfred Noyes

Saint George he slew the dragon,
　But he didn't shout hurray.
He dumped it in the wagon
　Just to clear the mess away.

But the wagoner he sold it
　To a showman at the Fair,
And when Saint George was told it,
　He was almost in despair.

For the people crowded round it
　To admire its teeth and claws,
But Saint George he was an Englishman
　And did not like applause.

"The creechah weighed a ton at most,"
　He muttered through his vizahd.
"I do not feel inclined to boast
　About that puny lizahd."

DADDY FELL INTO THE POND

Alfred Noyes

Everyone grumbled. The sky was grey.
We had nothing to do and nothing to say.
We were nearing the end of a dismal day,
And there seemed to be nothing beyond,
    THEN
 Daddy fell into the pond!

And everyone's face grew merry and bright,
And Timothy danced for sheer delight.
"Give me the camera, quick, oh quick!
He's crawling out of the duckweed." *Click!*

Then the gardener suddenly slapped his knee,
And doubled up, shaking silently,
And the ducks all quacked as if they were daft
And it sounded as if the old drake laughed.

O, there wasn't a thing that didn't respond
    WHEN
 Daddy fell into the pond!

THE LAMA

Ogden Nash

The one-l lama,
He's a priest.
The two-l llama,
He's a beast.
And I will bet
A silk pyjama
There isn't any
Three-l lllama.

PHIZZOG

Carl Sandburg

This face you got,
This here phizzog you carry around,
You never picked it out for yourself, at all, at all, — did you?
This here phizzog — somebody handed it to you — am I
right?
Somebody said, "Here's yours, now go see what you can do
with it."
Somebody slipped it to you and it was like a package marked:
"No goods exchanged after being taken away" —
This face you got.

THE RHINOCEROS

Ogden Nash

> The rhino is a homely beast,
> For human eyes he's not a feast.
> Farewell, farewell, you old rhinoceros,
> I'll stare at something less prepoceros.

THE SKUNK

Alfred Noyes

> Jacko the Skunk, in black and white,
> Walked up the road one summer night,
> And there he met, in gold and green,
> The biggest toad he'd ever seen.

> Said Mr. Skunk to Mr. Toad,
> "This is a strictly private road.
> You need no sign-post, I suppose?"
> "No," said the Toad, "I have my nose."

> "Wazzat?" "Oh my! Gee whiz! Gee whiz!"
> A private road? It surely is.
> Truer word was never said.
> Phew!!" cried Mr. Toad — and fled.

THE PUZZLED CENTIPEDE

Mrs. Edward Craster

The centipede was happy quite,
   Until a toad in fun
Said, "Pray, which leg goes after which?"
That worked her mind to such a pitch,
She lay distracted in a ditch
   Considering how to run.

THE PORPOISE

Ogden Nash

I kind of like the playful porpoise,
A healthy mind in a healthy corpus.
He and his cousin, the dolphin,
Why they like swimmin like I like golphin.

CELERY

Ogden Nash

Celery, raw,
Develops the jaw,
But celery, stewed,
Is more quietly chewed.

A SLEEPER FROM AMAZON

Unknown

A sleeper from the Amazon
Put nighties of his gra'mazon —
    The reason, that
    He was too fat
To get his own pajamazon.

I WISH THAT MY ROOM HAD A FLOOR

Gelett Burgess

I wish that my Room had a Floor;
I don't so much care for a Door,
    But this walking around
    Without touching the ground
Is getting to be quite a bore!

FRAGONARD

Ogden Nash

There was an old miser named Clarence,
Who simonized both of his parents.
"The initial expense,"
He remarked, "is immense,
But I'll save it on wearance and tearance."

ARE YOU A MARSUPIAL?

John Becker

Now are you a marsupial?
And have you a little pouch?
If I pinch it on the outside
Does something inside holler "Ouch!"?

THE TURKEY

Ogden Nash

There is nothing more perky
Than a masculine turkey.
When he struts he struts
With no ifs or buts.
When his face is apoplectic
His harem grows hectic
And when he gobbles
Their universe wobbles.

PEAS

Unknown

I eat my peas with honey,
I've done it all my life.
It makes the peas taste funny,
But it keeps them on my knife.

COVERING THE SUBJECT

Richard Armour

The turtle, clam, and crab as well
Are covered with a sturdy shell,
While fish, excepting maybe whales,
Are shingled fore and aft with scales.

Though most, perhaps, have not the plating
Of armadillos, it's worth stating
That animals at least have hides
That give them fairly firm outsides.

And yet that upright mammal, man,
Must get along as best he can
With nothing but a little skin
To keep his precious insides in.

I'VE GOT A NEW BOOK FROM MY GRANDFATHER HYDE

Leroy Jackson

I've got a new book from my Grandfather Hyde.
It's skin on the cover and paper inside,
And reads about Arabs and horses and slaves,
And tells how the Caliph of Bagdad behaves.
I'd not take a goat and a dollar beside
For the book I got from my Grandfather Hyde.

STAIRS

Oliver Herford

Here's to the man who invented stairs
And taught our feet to soar!
He was the first who ever burst
Into a second floor.

The world would be downstairs today
Had he not found the key;
So let his name go down to fame,
Whatever it may be.

ARITHMETIC

Carl Sandburg

Arithmetic is where numbers fly like pigeons in and out of
your head.

Arithmetic tells you how many you lose or win if you know
how many you had before you lost or won.

Arithmetic is seven eleven all good children go to heaven —
or five six bundle of sticks.

Arithmetic is numbers you squeeze from your head to your
hand to your pencil to your paper till you get the answer.

147

Arithmetic is where the answer is right and everything is nice
and you can look out the window and see the blue sky —
or the answer is wrong and you have to start all over and
try again and see how it comes out this time.

MISTER BEERS

Hugh Lofting

This is Mister Beers;
    And for forty-seven years
He's been digging in his garden like a miner.
    He isn't planting seeds
    Nor scratching up weeds,
He's trying to bore a tunnel down to China.

THE FROG

Hilaire Belloc

Be kind and tender to the Frog,
    And do not call him names,
As "Slimy-skin," or "Polly-wog,"
    Or likewise, "Ugly James,"

Or "Gape-a-grin," or "Toad-gone-wrong,"
    Or "Billy-Bandy-knees";
The Frog is justly sensitive
    To epithets like these.

No animal will more repay
    A treatment kind and fair,
At least, so lonely people say
Who keep a frog (and, by the way,
    They are extremely rare).

SEVEN LIMERICKS

Edward Lear

1

There was an Old Man with a beard,
Who said, 'It is just as I feared! —
    Two Owls and a Hen,
    Four Larks and a Wren,
Have all built their nests in my beard!'

2

There was an Old Lady of Chertsey,
Who made a remarkable curtesy:
    She twirled round and round
    Till she sank underground,
Which distressed all the people of Chertsey.

3

There was a Young Lady whose chin,
Resembled the point of a pin;
    So she had it made sharp,
    And purchased a harp,
And played several tunes with her chin.

4

There was an Old Man, who when little,
Fell casually into a Kettle;
    But, growing too stout,
    He could never get out,
So he passed all his life in that Kettle.

5

There was a Young Lady of Firle,
Whose Hair was addicted to curl;
    It curled up a Tree
    And all over the Sea,
That expensive Young Lady of Firle.

6

There was an Old Man of Ibreem,
Who suddenly threaten'd to scream;
    But they said, 'If you do,
    We will thump you quite blue,
You disgusting Old Man of Ibreem!'

7

There was an Old Person of Stroud,
Who was horribly jammed in a crowd;
    Some she slew with a kick,
    Some she scrunched with a stick,
That impulsive Old Person of Stroud.

HABITS OF THE HIPPOPOTAMUS

Arthur Guiterman

The hippopotamus is strong
    And huge of head and broad of bustle;
The limbs on which he rolls along
    Are big with hippopotomuscle.

He does not greatly care for sweets
    Like ice cream, apple pie, or custard,
But takes to flavor what he eats,
    A little hippopotomustard.

The hippopotamus is true
    To all his principles, and just;
He always tries his best to do
    The things one hippopotomust.

He never rides in trucks or trams,
    In taxicabs or omnibuses,
And so keeps out of traffic jams
    And other hippopotomusses.

HOW TO TELL THE WILD ANIMALS

Carolyn Wells

If ever you should go by chance
   To jungles in the East;
And if there should to you advance
   A large and tawny beast,
If he roars at you as you're dyin'
You'll know it is the Asian Lion.

Or if some time when roaming round,
   A noble wild beast greets you,
With black stripes on a yellow ground,
   Just notice if he eats you.
This simple rule may help you learn
The Bengal Tiger to discern.

If strolling forth, a beast you view,
   Whose hide with spots is peppered,
As soon as he has lept on you,
   You'll know it is the Leopard.
'Twill do no good to roar with pain,
He'll only lep and lep again.

If when you're walking round your yard,
   You meet a creature there,
Who hugs you very, very hard,
   Be sure it is the Bear.

If you have any doubt, I guess
He'll give you just one more caress.

Though to distinguish beasts of prey
   A novice might nonplus,
The Crocodiles you always may
   Tell from Hyenas thus:
Hyenas come with merry smiles;
But if they weep, they're Crocodiles.

The true Chameleon is small,
   A lizard sort of thing;
He hasn't any ears at all,
   And not a single wing.
If there is nothing in the tree,
'Tis the Chameleon you see.

"POET"

William Jay Smith

After, each, word, he, places, a, comma,
A, remarkable, effect, indeed,
It, gives, you, jitters, when, you, look,
It, gives, you, hiccoughs, when, you, read.

Let's
Look
Around

THE YOUNG DANDELION

Dinah Mulock Craik

I am a bold fellow
　　As ever was seen,
With my shield of yellow,
　　And my blade of green.

You may uproot me
　　From field and from lane;
Trample me, cut me,
　　I spring up again.

I never flinch, sir,
　　Wherever I dwell;
Give me an inch, sir,
　　I'll soon take an ell.

Drive me from the garden
　　In anger and pride,
I'll thrive and harden
　　By the roadside.

Not a bit fearful
Showing my face,
Always so cheerful,
　　In every place.

ROADWAYS

John Masefield

One road leads to London,
　One road runs to Wales,
My road leads me seawards
　To the white dipping sails.

One road leads to the river,
　As it goes singing slow;
My road leads to shipping
　Where the bronzed sailors go.

Leads me, lures me, calls me
　To salt green tossing sea;
A road without earth's road-dust
　Is the right road for me.

A wet road heaving, shining
　And wild with seagull's cries,
A mad salt sea-wind blowing
　The salt spray in my eyes.

My road calls me, lures me
　West, east, south, and north;
Most roads lead men homewards,
　My road leads me forth.

To add more miles to the tally
Of grey miles left behind,
In quest of that one beauty
God put me here to find.

A WANDERER'S SONG

John Masefield

A wind's in the heart of me, a fire's in my heels,
I am tired of brick and stone and rumbling wagon-wheels;
I hunger for the sea's edge, the limits of the land,
Where the wild old Atlantic is shouting on the sand.

Oh I'll be going, leaving the noises of the street,
To where a lifting foresail-foot is yanking at the sheet;
To a windy, tossing anchorage where yawls and ketches ride,
Oh I'll be going, going, until I meet the tide.

And first I'll hear the sea-wind, the mewing of the gulls,
The clucking, sucking of the sea about the rusty hulls,
The songs at the capstan in the hooker warping out,
And then the heart of me'll know I'm there or thereabout.

Oh I am tired of brick and stone, the heart of me is sick,
For windy, green, unquiet sea, the realm of Moby Dick;
And I'll be going, going, from the roaring of the wheels,
For a wind's in the heart of me, a fire's in my heels.

WIND

Aileen Fisher

The wind has lots of noises:
it sniffs,
it puffs,
it whines;
it rumbles like an ocean
through junipers and pines;
it whispers in the windows,
it howls,
it sings,
it hums;
it tells you VERY PLAINLY
every time it comes.

BOXES AND BAGS

Carl Sandburg

The bigger the box the more it holds.
Empty boxes hold the same as empty heads.
Enough small empty boxes thrown into a big empty box fill
    it full.
A half-empty box says, "Put more in."
A big enough box could hold the world.

Elephants need big boxes to hold a dozen elephant handker-
chiefs.
Fleas fold little handkerchiefs and fix them nice and neat in
flea handkerchief-boxes.
Bags lean against each other and boxes stand independent.
Boxes are square with corners unless round with circles.
Box can be piled on box and the bottom box says, "If you
will kindly take notice you will see it all rests on me."
Pile box on box and the top one says, "Who falls farthest if
or when we fall? I ask you."
Box people go looking for boxes and bag people go looking
for bags.

THERE ISN'T TIME

Eleanor Farjeon

There isn't time, there isn't time
To do the things I want to do,
With all the mountain-tops to climb,
And all the woods to wander through,
And all the seas to sail upon,
And everywhere there is to go,
And all the people, every one
Who lives upon the earth, to know.
There's only time, there's only time
To know a few, and do a few,
And then sit down and make a rhyme
About the rest I want to do.

THE TERM

William Carlos Williams

A rumpled sheet
of brown paper
about the length

and apparent bulk
of a man was
rolling with the

wind slowly over
and over in
the street as

a car drove down
upon it and
crushed it to

the ground. Unlike
a man it rose
again rolling

with the wind over
and over to be as
it was before.

SOUP

Carl Sandburg

I saw a famous man eating soup.
I say he was lifting a fat broth
Into his mouth with a spoon.
His name was in the newspapers that day
Spelled out in tall black headlines
And thousands of people were talking about him.

When I saw him,
He sat bending his head over a plate
Putting soup in his mouth with a spoon.

PRIMER LESSON

Carl Sandburg

Look out how you use proud words.
When you let proud words go, it is not easy to call them
   back.
They wear long boots, hard boots; they walk off proud; they
   can't hear you calling —
Look out how you use proud words.

THE COMFORTABLE APPLE TREES

Grace Taber Hallock

Apple trees are made to sing in,
Climb and sit and read and swing in.
Apple trees are made to rest in,
And for happy birds to nest in.

LOOKING UP AT
AIRPLANES, ALWAYS

Rolfe Humphries

High overhead,
High overhead the planes go over
I lift my eyes
To see them, always.

Having been there,
Having been there at that great height
I rise up swiftly,
And there again.

Like dragon-flies,
Like dragon-flies how brief their season!
A hundred hours,
So I have heard.

AEOLUS

Rolfe Humphries

I am Aeolus, who keep
Or try to keep, my winds asleep.
Good watchman that I am, I know
One at a time alone may blow,
Whose wildly jealous kin will rave
Within their black and stifling cave
Unless I turn them into sheep.

And once this miracle is done,
I love my freedom in the sun
Where I may sit, on holiday,
With friends who happen by the way,
And talk and smile, until I hear
Behind my back the sound I fear,
The ominous confusion, — Hark,
My winds are fighting in the dark!

Forgive me if I turn and go
Without one decent word. I know
How rude I seem to every one,
But I must do what must be done,
Unseen and single-handed, fight
Those stormy devils in the night,
Unseen and single-handed, save
The world from ruin in my cave.
Responsible and tyrannous,
Pity me. I am Aeolus.

VIEW

Josephine Miles

When the last Pullman of the day pulls into the Grand Can-
    yon station,
And in the sunset light the passengers come
One after another over the platform, over the sward to the
    rim
Line up, look down,
             The shadows loom
Fast into pools bluer than morning,
Abyss drawn by its river miles from home,
And they look into it as into a family album,
Where every idiosyncracy has room.

MAROONED

Rachel Field

      Narrow River is salty blue,
        The thorn trees shine and blur.
    Along the humped backs of the dunes
        Sand grass grows thick as fur.
    Gulls wheel and settle like falling snow,
        White flakes in the summer sun.
    But darkly tilted, its mast awry,
        Is an old ship's skeleton, —
    Marooned as never a ship should be,
        Prow turned inland and stern to the sea.

MIRACLES

Walt Whitman

Why, who makes much of a miracle?
As to me I know of nothing else but miracles,
Whether I walk the streets of Manhattan,
Or dart my sight over the roofs of houses toward the sky,
Or wade with naked feet along the beach just in the edge of
    the water,
Or stand under trees in the woods,
Or talk by day with any one I love. . . .
Or sit at table at dinner with the rest,
Or look at strangers opposite me riding in the car.
Or watch honey-bees busy around the hive of a summer fore-
    noon,
Or animals feeding in the fields,
Or birds, or the wonderfulness of insects in the air,
Or the wonderfulness of the sundown, or of stars shining so
    quiet and bright,
Or the exquisite delicate thin curve of the new moon in
    spring;
These with the rest, one and all, are to me miracles,
The whole referring, yet each distinct and in its place.

To me every hour of the light and dark is a miracle,
Every cubic inch of space is a miracle,
Every square yard of the surface of the earth is spread with
    the same,
Every foot of the interior swarms with the same.

To me the sea is a continual miracle,
The fishes that swim — the rocks — the motion of the waves
    — the ships with men in them,
What stranger miracles are there?

I'LL TELL YOU HOW THE SUN ROSE

Emily Dickinson

I'll tell you how the sun rose, —
A ribbon at a time.
The steeples swam in amethyst,
The news like squirrels ran,

The hills untied their bonnets,
The bobolinks begun.
Then I said softly to myself,
"That must have been the sun!"

But how he set, I know not.
There seemed a purple stile
Which little yellow boys and girls
Were climbing all the while.

Till when they reached the other side,
A dominie in gray
Put gently up the evening bars,
And led the flock away.

THE PEACOCK OF JAVA

William Jay Smith

I thought of the mariners of Solomon,
Who, on one of their long voyages, came
   On that rare bird, the peacock
   Of Java, which brings, even
To the tree of heaven, heaven.

How struggling upward through the dark
   Lianas, they beheld the tree,
   And in the tree, the fan
That would become a king's embroidery.

How they turned and on the quiet
   Water then set sail
   For home, the peacock's tail
Committed to the legends of the sea.

THE SHIPS OF YULE

Bliss Carman

When I was just a little boy,
Before I went to school,
I had a fleet of forty sail,
I called the Ships of Yule;

168

Of every rig, from rakish brig
And gallant barkentine,
To little Fundy fishing boats
With gunwales painted green.

They used to go on trading trips
Around the world for me,
For though I had to stay on shore
My heart was on the sea.

They stopped at every port of call
From Babylon to Rome,
To load with all the lovely things
We never had at home;

With elephants and ivory
Bought from the King of Tyre,
And shells and silk and sandal-wood
That sailor men admire;

With figs and dates from Samarcand,
And squatty ginger-jars,
And scented silver amulets
From Indian bazaars;

With sugar-cane from Port of Spain,
And monkeys from Ceylon,
And paper lanterns from Peking
With painted dragons on;

With cocoanuts from Zanzibar,
And pines from Singapore;
And when they had unloaded these
They could go back for more.

And even after I was big
And had to go to school,
My mind was often far away
Aboard the Ships of Yule.

PRETTY WORDS

Elinor Wylie

Poets make pets of pretty, docile words:
I love smooth words, like gold-enameled fish
Which circle slowly with a silken swish,
And tender ones, like downy-feathered birds:
Words shy and dappled, deep-eyed deer in herds,
Come to my hand, and playful if I wish,
Or purring softly at a silver dish,
Blue Persian kittens, fed on cream and curds.

I love bright words, words up and singing early;
Words that are luminous in the dark, and sing;
Warm lazy words, white cattle under trees;
I love words opalescent, cool and pearly,
Like midsummer moths, and honied words like bees,
Gilded and sticky, with a little sting.

IT'S PLEASANT TO THINK

Elizabeth Coatsworth

Sitting here
in our usual chairs,
it's pleasant to think
of polar bears,

of polar bears
amid ice floes,
dog-sleds and broad-faced
Eskimos.

It's pleasant to think,
on the other hand,
of monkeys who live
in a tropical land,

and chatter and peer
at the forest floor,
where elephants stamp
and lions roar.

As far as the strong-winged
eagles fly,
our frail thoughts climb
to pierce the sky,

and deep in the sea
as fishes sink,
a child may go
if a child will think.

High and low
and far and wide,
swift and nimble,
a thought will ride.

But what it brings back
at the saddle bow
only the mind that sent it
will know.

YOUNG SEA

Carl Sandburg

The sea is never still.
It pounds on the shore
Restless as a young heart,
Hunting.

The sea speaks
And only the stormy hearts
Know what it says:
It is the face
    of a rough mother speaking.

The sea is young.
One storm cleans all the hoar
And loosens the age of it.
I hear it laughing, reckless.

They love the sea,
Men who ride on it
And know they will die
Under the salt of it.

Let only the young come,
   says the sea.
Let them kiss my face
   And hear me.
I am the last word
   and I tell
Where storms and stars come from.

WILD HORSES

Carl Sandburg

Roots, go deep: wrap your coils; fasten your knots:
Fix a loop far under, a four-in-hand far under.
The wind drives wild horses, gnashers, plungers:
   Go deep, roots.
Hold your four-in-hand knots against all wild horses.

THE MOON

Elizabeth Coatsworth

The fields are spread like tablecloths
   which the Moon puts out to dry,
and she has washed the high hilltops
   and whitened all the sky.

Now pale, serene, and weary,
   she glances round the night.
Is every flower silver?
   Is each wild eyeball bright?

SMALL SONG

Frances Frost

Morning is a little lass,
Her gay head yellow-curled,
Who jumps a rope of knotted flowers
Across the waking world.

Evening is a little boy
With dark wind-ruffled hair,
Who skips the stars like stones across
The darkling pond of air.

THINGS TO LEARN ABOUT

John Becker

Black and white
Mine and thine
Big and little
In and out
These are things
To learn about.

Black is always black
But white is black at night.
Mine is often thine,
Thine is sometimes mine.
You are bigger to a pea
Than you are smaller to a tree.
In is that-a-way
When you're coming this-a-way,
But in is out
When you're going that-a-way.

Black and white
Mine and thine
Big and little
In and out
These are things
To learn about.

THE HILLS

Rachel Field

Sometimes I think the hills
That loom across the harbor
Lie there like sleeping dragons,
Crouched one above another,
With trees for tufts of fur
Growing all up and down
The ridges and humps of their backs,
And orange cliffs for claws
Dipped in the sea below.
Sometimes a wisp of smoke
Rises out of the hollows,
As if in their dragon sleep
They dreamed of strange old battles.

What if the hills should stir
Some day and stretch themselves,
Shake off the clinging trees
And all the clustered houses?

FIRE ON THE HEARTH

Rowena Bennett

A goblin lives in the chimney place,
A goblin squats on the brick.
He wrinkles his red and ugly face
As he crunches a great pine stick.
He crunches a stick and he gnaws a coal,
And if he could leap from his sooty hole,
He would gobble the table and all the chairs
And hiss aloud as he rushed upstairs.
He would burst through the roof and kick down the wall
And then we should have no house at all.

Oh, I'm glad that the goblin with all his tricks
Is trapped by a grate in his hole of bricks!

I STOOD UPON A STAR

Sara Teasdale

I stretched my mind until I stood
Out in space, upon a star;
I looked, and saw the flying earth
Where seven planets are.

Delicately interweaving
　　Like fireflies on a moist June night,
The planetoids among the planets
　　Played for their own delight.

I watched earth putting off her winter
　　And slipping into green;
I saw the dark side of the moon
　　No man has ever seen.

Like shining wheels in an opened watch
　　They all revolved with soundless motion;
Earth sparkled like a rain-wet flower,
　　Bearing her petals, plain and ocean.

THE FREIGHT TRAIN

Rowena Bennett

The slow freight wriggles along the rail
With a red caboose for a lashing tail,
With a one-eyed engine for a head
The slow freight follows the river bed.

He moves like a snake that has grown too fat,
One that has swallowed a frog and a rat;

But a giant of snakes is the moving freight
And these are some of the things he ate:

A herd of sheep and a hundred hens
And dozens of pigs with crates for pens
And horses and cows by the sixes and tens;
And these are some of the things he drank:
Oil and gasoline by the tank,
Milk by the gallon and cream by the pail —
No wonder he moves at the pace of a snail.

SMOKE ANIMALS

Rowena Bennett

Out of the factory chimney, tall
Great black animals like to crawl.
They push each other and shove and crowd.
They nose the wind and they claw a cloud,
And they walk right out on the empty sky
With their tails all curled and their heads held high;
But their terrible fierceness is just a joke
For they're only made of a puff of smoke.

I LIKE TO SEE IT LAP THE MILES

Emily Dickinson

I like to see it lap the miles,
And lick the valleys up,
And stop to feed itself at tanks;
And then, prodigious, step

Around a pile of mountains,
And, supercilious, peer
In shanties by the sides of roads;
And then a quarry pare

To fit its sides, and crawl between,
Complaining all the while
In horrid, hooting stanza;
Then chase itself down hill

And neigh like Boanerges;
Then, punctual as a star,
Stop — docile and omnipotent —
At its own stable door.

SHINY

James Reeves

Shiny are the chestnut leaves
   Before they unfold.
The inside of a buttercup
   Is like polished gold.
A pool in the sunshine
   Is bright too,
And a fine silver shilling
   When it is new.
But the round, full moon,
   So clear and white,
How brightly she shines
   On a winter night!
Slowly she rises,
   Higher and higher,
With a cold clear light
   Like ice on fire.

THE HUNGRY WAVES

Dorothy Aldis

The hungry waves along the shore
Chase each other with a roar.

They raise their heads and, wide and high,
Toss their hair against the sky.

They show their teeth in rows of white
And open up their jaws to bite.

UNDER GROUND

James Reeves

In the deep kingdom under ground
There is no light and little sound.

Down below the earth's green floor
The rabbit and the mole explore.

The quarrying ants run to and fro
To make their populous empires grow.

Do they, as I pass overhead,
Stop in their work to hear my tread?

Some creatures sleep and do not toil,
Secure and warm beneath the soil.

Sometimes a fork or spade intrudes
Upon their earthy solitudes.

Downward the branching tree-roots spread
Into the country of the dead.

Deep down, the buried rocks and stones
Are like the earth's gigantic bones.

In the dark kingdom under ground
How many marvellous things are found!

GRIM AND GLOOMY

James Reeves

Oh, grim and gloomy,
So grim and gloomy
Are the caves beneath the sea.
Oh, rare but roomy
And bare and boomy,
Those salt sea caverns be.

Oh, slim and slimy
Or grey and grimy
Are the animals of the sea.
Salt and oozy
And safe and snoozy
The caves where those animals be.

Hark to the shuffling,
Huge and snuffling,
Ravenous, cavernous, great sea-beasts!
But fair and fabulous,
Tintinnabulous,
Gay and fabulous are their feasts.

Ah, but the queen of the sea,
The querulous, perilous sea!
How the curls of her tresses
The pearls on her dresses,
Sway and swirl in the waves,
How cozy and dozy,
How sweet ring-a-rosy
Her bower in the deep-sea-caves!

Oh, rare but roomy
And bare and boomy
Those caverns under the sea,
And grave and grandiose,
Safe and sandiose
The dens of her denizens be.

THE MAP

Elizabeth Bishop

Land lies in water; it is shadowed green.
Shadows, or are they shallows, at its edges

showing the line of long sea-weeded ledges
where weeds hang to the simple blue from green.
Or does the land lean down to lift the sea from under,
drawing it unperturbed around itself?
Along the fine tan sandy shelf
is the land tugging at the sea from under?

The shadow of Newfoundland lies flat and still.
Labrador's yellow, where the moony Eskimo
has oiled it. We can stroke these lovely bays,
under a glass as if they were expected to blossom,
or as if to provide a clean cage for invisible fish.
The names of seashore towns run out to sea,
the names of cities cross the neighbouring mountains
— the printer here experiencing the same excitement
as when emotion too far exceeds its cause.
These peninsulas take the water between thumb and finger
like women feeling for the smoothness of yard-goods.

Mapped waters are more quiet than the land is,
lending the land their waves' own conformation:
and Norway's hare runs south in agitation,
profiles investigate the sea, where land is.
Are they assigned, or can the countries pick their colours?
Who suits the character or the native waters best.
Topography displays no favourites; North's as near as West.
More delicate than the historians' are the map-makers'
    colours.

Days
and
Holidays

THE MONTHS

Sara Coleridge

January brings the snow,
Makes our feet and fingers glow.

February brings the rain,
Thaws the frozen lakes again.

March brings breezes sharp and chill,
Shakes the dancing daffodil.

April brings the primrose sweet,
Scatters daisies at our feet.

May brings flocks of pretty lambs,
Sporting by their fleecy dams.

June brings tulips, lilies, roses,
Fills the children's hands with posies.

Hot July brings cooling showers,
Apricots, and gillyflowers.

August brings the sheaves of corn,
Then the harvest home is borne.

Warm September brings the fruit,
Sportsmen then begin to shoot.

Fresh October brings the pheasant,
Then to gather nuts is pleasant.

Dull November brings the blast —
Hark! the leaves are whirling fast.

Cold December brings the sleet,
Blazing fire, and Christmas treat.

FOR FEBRUARY TWELFTH

Muriel M. Gessner

Today we think of that great man
    Who, when a boy named Abe,
    Lived in our country — in the West,
And, growing like the corn he hoed,
    Came to overtop the rest
        Of all his mates.

He was so very fast and sure
In all the sports and games.
    He won the high jumps and the races.
In doing work, he too was skilled.

He swung an ax. He marked the spaces
   For cabin homes.

He helped fetch water from the spring,
And cut pegs with his knife
   To nail the rugged hand-hewn boards
For fitting round the new-made doors.
     He knew wood creatures — where bees stored
       Their golden honey.

At dusk he saw deer drinking at the stream;
Heard whir of turkey wings,
   As in the quiet woods he wandered.
Often in his small loft room
   He lay and thought and pondered
   On right and wrong.

He needed books, so walked for them
Fifty miles or more.
   To honest be, and just, and kind
To him seemed most important.
   He used his body and his mind,
     And ever grew.

He knew and loved both God and man;
He served his country well;
   His deeds brought freedom to the slave,
His words brought hope to many men.
   The greatness of his life he gave
     To all the world.

A VALENTINE

Eleanor Hammond

Frost flowers on the window glass,
Hopping chickadees that pass,
Bare old elms that bend and sway,
Pussy willows, soft and gray.

Silver clouds across the sky,
Lacy snowflakes flitting by,
Icicles like fringe in line —
That is Outdoor's valentine.

WHEN

Dorothy Aldis

In February there are days,
Blue, and nearly warm,
When horses switch their tails and ducks
Go quacking through the farm.
When all the world turns round to feel
The sun upon its back —
When winter lifts a little bit
And Spring peeks through the crack.

191

VALENTINE

C. W. T.

> No early buds of laughing spring
> Upon this day to thee I bring
> > Sweet Valentine.

> But thoughts as pure as snowdrops fair
> My loving heart to thee would bear,
> > My Valentine.

GETTYSBURG ADDRESS

Abraham Lincoln

Four score and seven years ago our fathers brought forth on this continent, a new nation, conceived in liberty, and dedicated to the proposition that all men are created equal.

Now we are engaged in a great civil war, testing whether that nation, or any nation so conceived and so dedicated, can long endure. We are met on a great battlefield of that war. We have come to dedicate a portion of that field, as a final resting place for those who here gave their lives that that nation might live. It is altogether fitting and proper that we should do this.

But, in a larger sense, we can not dedicate — we can not consecrate — we can not hallow — this ground. The brave men, living and dead, who struggled here have consecrated it, far above our poor power to add or detract. The world will little note, nor long remember, what we say here, but it can never forget what they did here. It is for us the living, rather, to be dedicated here to the unfinished work which they who fought here have thus far so nobly advanced. It is rather for us to be here dedicated to the great task remaining before us — that from these honored dead we take increased devotion to that cause for which they gave the last full measure of devotion — that we here highly resolve that these dead shall not have died in vain — that this nation, under God, shall have a new birth of freedom — and that government of the people, by the people, and for the people, shall not perish from the earth.

WASHINGTON

James Russell Lowell

Soldier and statesman, rarest unison;
High-poised example of great duties done
Simply as breathing, a world's honors worn
As life's indifferent gifts to all men born;
Dumb for himself, unless it were to God,
But for his barefoot soldiers eloquent,
Tramping the snow to coral where they trod,
Held by his awe in hollow-eyed content;
Modest, yet firm as Nature's self; unblamed
Save by the men his nobler temper shamed;

Never seduced through show of present good
By other than unsetting lights to steer
New-trimmed in Heaven, nor than his steadfast mood
More steadfast, far from rashness as from fear;
Rigid, but with himself first, grasping still
In swerveless poise the wave-beat helm of will;
Not honored then or now because he wooed
The popular voice, but that he still withstood;
Broad-minded, higher-souled, there is but one,
Who was all this and ours, and all men's — WASHINGTON.

GEORGE WASHINGTON

James S. Tippett

George Washington, the farmer,
Loved his house and land;
Loved his horses, sheep and cows
And gardens he had planned;
Had his slaves and servants
To run at his command;
Lived in white Mount Vernon.
Oh, but he was grand.

George Washington, the fighter,
Knew the Indian's ways;
Led Virginia volunteers
In bloody forest frays.

George Washington, the rebel,
Lived among his men;
Fought the British King's men
Again and yet again;
Slipped across the Delaware;
Grieved at Valley Forge;
Crafty, tender-hearted chief,
Was General George.

Called to serve his country,
As President he came;
Was a man like other men,
Bore his share of blame;
Made his mark upon the world,
An honored, special name;
Helped his country at the start
To do the very same.

And every year upon this day
The land he helped to free
Thinks about George Washington
And makes bold plans to be
In all its Valley Forges
As resolute as he.

JUST A MILE BEYOND

Aileen Fisher

Winter's house is cold and white,
but just a mile beyond
Spring lives in a new green house
beside a sparkly pond.

A STILL DAY

Joseph Cherwinski

The day recedes in white
long vistas toward the night,

long lonely slabs of snow
carved in a crystal blow,

shining in gold, in bronze,
fretted with purple ponds,

silent but for the creak
the sparrow-hinges speak,

wedging the door of spring
toward opening. . . .

196

MAPLE FEAST

Frances Frost

Into the big-flaked sugar-snow
The crystal-gathering sledges go.

Stumbling through silver to my knees,
I shout among the maple trees,

Tilt gleaming buckets icy cold
Till I am full as I can hold

Of clear bright sap, until I feel
Like a maple tree from head to heel!

Then to the sugarhouse I run
Where syrup, golden as the sun,

Is boiling in the crisp March air.
And I, as daft as a baby bear,

Eat, till my buttons burst asunder
From maple sweetness, maple wonder!

SPRING FAMILIES

Frances Frost

March shakes the pussy willows out
Of their brown wintry beds,
And gets the first-grass-children up
And combs their tousled heads.

April mixes silver rain
And golden sun to suds
To wash the scarlet petticoats
Of the little maple buds.

And May sews round bright dandelion
Buttons on the hills,
And ties their yellow bonnets on
The youngest daffodils.

A RAINY DAY

Joseph C. Lincoln

Kind of LIKE a stormy day, take it all together, —
Don't believe I'd want it just only pleasant weather;
If the sky was allers blue, guess I'd be complainin'
And a-pesterin' around, wishin' it was rainin'.

Like a stormy mornin' now, with the water dashin'
From the eaves and from the spouts, foamin' and a-splashin',
With the leaves and twigs around, shinin' wet and drippin',
Shakin' in the wind with drops every-which-way skippin'.

Like to see the gusts of rain, where there's naught to hinder,
Sail acrost the fields and come "spat" against the winder,
Streakin' down along the panes, floodin' sills and ledges,
Makin' little fountains, like, in the sash's edges.

Like to see the brooks and ponds dimpled up all over,
Like to see the di'mon's shine on the bendin' clover,
Like to see the happy ducks in the puddles sailin',
And the stuck-up rooster all draggled, wet and trailin'.

But I like it best inside, with the fire a-gleamin',
And myself, with chores all done, settin' round and dreamin',
With the kitten on my knee, and the kettle hummin',
And the raindrops on the roof, "Home, Sweet Home" a-
    drummin'.

Kind of like a stormy day, take it all together,
Don't believe I'd want it just only pleasant weather;
If the sky was allers blue, guess I'd be complainin',
And a-pesterin' around, wishin' it was rainin'.

PUSSY-WILLOWS

Aileen Fisher

Spring, Spring,
everything
you do is new and shiny.
Who, who
teaches you
to think of things as tiny
as all those velvet
willow cats
in furry coats
and furry hats
astride a twig
like acrobats,
soft, and sleek, and shiny?

APRIL FOOL

Elizabeth Coatsworth

"I saw an elephant walking down the road.
He had a book and was going to school.
He carried a satchel to hold his lunch —
APRIL FOOL!

200

"I saw your grandmother and your aunt
Fishing for suckers in the mill-stream pool.
They'd caught a dozen and maybe more —
APRIL FOOL!

"Mercy! whoever has mended your shirt?
The needle's still there and the thread and the spool.
Didn't you feel them there at the hem?
APRIL FOOL!"

IN THE HEART OF A SEED

Kate L. Brown

In the heart of a seed,
    Buried deep, so deep,
A dear little plant
    Lay fast asleep.

"Wake," said the sunshine,
    "And creep to the light;"
"Wake," said the voice
    Of the raindrops bright.

The little plant heard,
    And it rose to see
What the beautiful
    Outside world might be.

201

PEEPERS

Melville Cane

Over marsh and swamp and pond
Fabulous April waves her wand!
Winter dissolves.

Lowlands evolve,
Shed their frozen lethargy,
Seethe with panting urgency.

The countryside is rife
With life,
Abounds
With rising sounds.

From every luscious soggy bog
The froglets fling their piping song.

Like frisky youngsters out of school,
Their trebles shrill from pool to pool,
Their peeps explode and dynamite
The innocent frontiers of the night.

FOUR LITTLE FOXES

Lew Sarett

Speak gently, Spring, and make no sudden sound;
For in my windy valley, yesterday, I found
New-born foxes squirming on the ground —
                    Speak gently.

Walk softly, March, forbear the bitter blow;
Her feet within a trap, her blood upon the snow,
The four little foxes saw their mother go —
                    Walk softly.

Go lightly, Spring, oh, give them no alarm;
When I covered them with boughs to shelter them from
    harm,
The thin blue foxes suckled at my arm —
                    Go lightly.

Step softly, March, with your rampant hurricane;
Nuzzling one another, and whimpering with pain,
The new little foxes are shivering in the rain —
                    Step softly.

SEEDS

Walter de la Mare

The seeds I sowed —
For weeks unseen —
Have pushed up pygmy
Shoots of green;
So frail you'd think
The tiniest stone
Would never let
A glimpse be shown.

But no; a pebble
Near them lies,
At least a cherry-stone
In size,
Which that mere sprout
Has heaved away,
To bask in sunshine,
See the Day.

THE NEW GARDEN

Reginald Arkell

It is a most exciting thing
To take a garden in the Spring:

To wonder what its borders hold;
What secrets lurk beneath the mold?

What kinds of roses you have got;
Whether the lilac blooms, or not.

Whether the peach tree, on the wall,
Has ever had a peach at all. . . .

It is a most exciting thing
To take a garden in the Spring;

And live in such delicious doubt,
Until the final flower is out.

HAYFIELD

Aileen Fisher

I like to see the wind
go racing through the hay:
it's just like a green fire
galloping away.
It's a field full of green flames
licking at the hill.
And then it's just a hayfield
. . . when the wind is still.

I like to see the wind
go swelling through the grass:
it's just like an ocean
when the green waves pass.
It's a green sea of billows
rolling toward the town.
And then it's just a hayfield
. . . when the wind dies down.

TULIP

William Jay Smith

A slender goblet wreathed in flame,
From Istanbul the flower came
And brought its beauty, and its name.

Now as I lift it up, that fire
Sweeps on from dome to golden spire
Until the East is all aflame:

By curving petals held entire
In cup of ceremonial fire,
Magnificence within a frame.

AN ARBOR DAY TREE

Unknown

"Dear little tree that we plant today,
What will you be when we're old and gray?"

"The savings bank of the squirrel and mouse,
For the robin and wren an apartment house;

The dressing room of the butterfly's ball;
The locust and katydid's concert hall;

The schoolboy's ladder in pleasant June,
The schoolgirl's tent in the July noon;

And my leaves shall whisper them merrily
A tale of the children who planted me."

207

LOVELIEST OF TREES

A. E. Housman

Loveliest of trees, the cherry now
Is hung with bloom along the bough,
And stands about the woodland ride
Wearing white for Eastertide.

Now, of my threescore years and ten,
Twenty will not come again,
And take from seventy springs a score,
It only leaves me fifty more.

And since to look at things in bloom
Fifty springs are little room,
About the woodlands I will go
To see the cherry hung with snow.

ALL DRESSED UP FOR EASTER

Aileen Fisher

All dressed up for Easter
in yellow, green and white —
but I've got a blister
'cause my shoes are tight!

PLANTING A TREE

Nancy Byrd Turner

Firm in the good brown earth
   Set we our little tree.
Clear dews will freshen it,
Cool rain will feed it,
Sun will be warming it
As warmth is needed.
Winds will blow round it free —
   Take root, good tree!

Slowly, as days go on,
   These boughs will stouter be,
Leaves will unfurl on them,
And, when spring comes to them,
Blossoms uncurl on them,
Birds make their homes in them,
Shadows stretch wide and free —
   Grow well, good tree!

SMELLS

Kathryn Worth

Through all the frozen winter
My nose has grown most lonely

For lovely, lovely, colored smells
That come in springtime only.

The purple smell of lilacs,
The yellow smell that blows
Across the air of meadows
Where bright forsythia grows.

The tall pink smell of peach trees,
The low white smell of clover,
And everywhere the great green smell
Of grass the whole world over.

MAY MOON

Olive Driver

May moon,
Waxing soon
Like a lovely,
Swelling tune!

Whitely Shine
On wood and lea,
Touching birch
And cherry tree.

With a silence
Bright and bold
And the season's
Latest cold.

May moon,
Waning soon,
Slipping slowly
Into June!

THE FLAG GOES BY

Henry Holcomb Bennett

Hats off!
Along the street there comes
A blare of bugles, a ruffle of drums,
A flash of colour beneath the sky:
Hats off!
The flag is passing by!

Blue and crimson and white it shines,
Over the steel-tipped, ordered lines.
Hats off!
The colours before us fly;
But more than the flag is passing by:

Sea-fights and land-fights, grim and great,
Fought to make and to save the State;
Weary marches and sinking ships;
Cheers of victory on dying lips;

Days of plenty and years of peace;
March of a strong land's swift increase;
Equal justice, right and law,
Stately honour and reverend awe;

Sign of a nation, great and strong
To ward her people from foreign wrong;
Pride and glory and honour, — all
Live in the colours to stand or fall.

Hats off!
Along the street there comes
A blare of bugles, a ruffle of drums;
And loyal hearts are beating high:
Hats off!
The flag is passing by!

SCHOOL IS OUT

Frances Frost

School is out, and we say good-by
to teacher, songs, and books,
and hustle through the sunny day
toward buttercups and brooks!

"Good-by until next fall!" we cry
and tumble through the town,
and change to shorts and bathing suits
to get us freckle-brown.

We've learned all that we can this year
in school. Our classrooms now
are blueberry hill and apple tree
and sweet and shadowy mow.

We'll learn deep woods and river roads,
we'll clamber pasture bars;
and night will be our blackboard, marked
with well-earned, golden stars!

AMERICA FOR ME

Henry van Dyke

'Tis fine to see the Old World, and travel up and down
Among the famous palaces and cities of renown,
To admire the crumbly castles and the statues of the kings —
But now I think I've had enough of antiquated things.

So it's home again, and home again, America for me!
My heart is turning home again, and there I long to be.
In the land of youth and freedom beyond the ocean bars,
Where the air is full of sunlight and the flag is full of stars.

Oh, London is a man's town, there's power in the air;
And Paris is a woman's town, with flowers in her hair;
And it's sweet to dream in Venice, and it's great to study
    Rome;
But when it comes to living there is no place like home.

I like the German fir-woods, in green battalions drilled;
I like the gardens of Versailles with dashing fountains filled;
But, oh, to take your hand, my dear, and ramble for a day
In the friendly western woodland where Nature has her way!

I know that Europe's wonderful, yet something seems to
    lack:

The Past is too much with her, and the people looking back.
But the glory of the Present is to make the Future free, —
We love our land for what she is and what she is to be.

Oh, it's home again, and home again, America for me!
I want a ship that's westward bound to plough the rolling sea,
To the blessed Land of Room Enough beyond the ocean bars,
Where the air is full of sunlight and the flag is full of stars.

A HOT-WEATHER SONG

Don Marquis

I feel so exceedingly lazy,
    I neglect what I oughtn't to should!
My notion of work is so hazy
    That I couldn't to toil if I would!

I feel so exceedingly silly
    That I say all I shouldn't to ought!
And my mind is as frail as a lily;
    It would break with the weight of a thought!

ALIKE

Dorothy Aldis

On summer days a rustling tree
Could be the sighing of the sea,
And waves on any rocky shore
Sound like trees bowed down before
The wind, Oh, it is hard to say
Which is leaves and which is spray.

SUMMER MOONLIGHT

Patience Strong

The room looks strange when moonlight falls,
    Across the windows and the walls,
The mirror frames a thousand stars,
    The floor is ribbed with silver bars.

Around the panes the roses trail,
    Their phantom blossoms, cool and pale.
The tree whose branches touch the sill,
    Stands breathless, watching, very still.

I lie in silence, wide awake,
    Afraid to stir lest I should break
The spell that is upon the night,
    The peace of shadow and of light.

SUMMER RAIN

Elizabeth Coatsworth

What could be lovelier than to hear
    the summer rain
    cutting across the heat, as scythes
    cut across grain?
    Falling upon the steaming roof
    with sweet uproar,
    tapping and rapping wildly
    at the door?

No, do not lift the latch,
    but through the pane
    we'll stand and watch the circus pageant
    of the rain,
    and see the lightning, like a tiger,
    striped and dread,
    and hear the thunder cross the shaken sky
    with elephant tread.

SUMMER STARS

Carl Sandburg

Bend low again, night of summer stars.
So near you are, sky of summer stars,
So near, a long-arm man can pick off stars,
Pick off what he wants in the sky bowl,
So near you are, summer stars,
So near, strumming, strumming,
So lazy and hum-strumming.

PASTORAL

Edna St. Vincent Millay

If it were only still! —
With far away the shrill
Crying of a cock;
Or the shaken bell
From a cow's throat
Moving through the bushes;
Or the soft shock
Of wizened apples falling
From an old tree
In a forgotten orchard
Upon the hill rock!

Oh, grey hill,
Where the grazing herd
Licks the purple blossom,
Crops the spiky weed!
Oh, stony pasture,
Where the tall mullein
Stands up so sturdy
On its little seed!

AUTUMN

William Jay Smith

The color of stone when leaves are yellow,
Comes the squirrel, a capital C,
With tail atilt like a violincello,
Comes the squirrel musically.

Quick, quick, quick, the notes fly
Up, and off the 'cello floats
Over the lawn where children play,
Over the matchstick-masted boats.

Under way in the lagoon,
Down the steps, the rock walls,
Over a Triton, bearing shells,
Music flows, water falls.

Time, old hunchback, worn and yellow,
Whets his scythe on weathered stone;
While azure mists invade the hollow,
And turkey-red the leaves come down.

AUTUMN RAIN

Aileen Fisher

Autumn rain has lots of fun
being so many things in one:

It can dive from way up high
through the ocean of the sky.

It can threaten half a day,
then pack up and move away.

It can change to flakes of snow,
somersaulting as they go.

It can turn to icy rain,
wrapping streets in cellophane.

It can drive us to despair
as we watch and sniff the air,
wondering WHAT we ought to wear.

WATCHING THE MOON

David McCord

September evenings such as these
The moon hides early in the trees,
And when we drive along the shore
I think I miss the trees the more
Because the moon is coming down
Beyond the branches and will drown.

MARIGOLD

Louise Townsend Nicholl

It is a cold courage
But the sun will warm it.
By noon it will be glowing like a garnet.
I will cover my hands with marigold and petunia,
Rough Autumn smells which sting,
And for a sign, a signet,
I will wear a hornet,
A glistening pointed hornet, for a ring.

BEECH LEAVES

James Reeves

In autumn down the beechwood path
   The leaves lie thick upon the ground.
It's there I love to kick my way
   And hear their crisp and crashing sound.

I am a giant, and my steps
   Echo and thunder to the sky.
How the small creatures of the woods
   Must quake and cower as I pass by!

This brave and merry noise I make
   In summer also when I stride
Down to the shining, pebbly sea
   And kick the frothing waves aside.

COLOR

Melville Cane

These leaves, so deeply and so lately green,
All summer long have laid
On us their steady screen
Of shade.

A color serves to cool us in our need.

Now, beneath a blander sun,
Its mission done,
The faithful hue recedes
And abdicates the scene.

An airier season dawns and supersedes.

October's
Crisp elixir
Transmutes all heaven with irradiance
Of scarlet flame and golden fire
Before the leaves expire,
Before the final fluttering dance
In the maples, and before the oak-tree dons
Its somber bronze.

GATHERING LEAVES

Robert Frost

Spades take up leaves
No better than spoons,
And bags full of leaves
Are light as balloons.

I make a great noise
Of rustling all day
Like rabbit and deer
Running away.

But the mountains I raise
Elude my embrace,
Flowing over my arms
And into my face.

I may load and unload
Again and again
Till I fill the whole shed,
And what have I then?

Next to nothing for weight,
And since they grew duller
From contact with earth,
Next to nothing for color.

Next to nothing for use.
But a crop is a crop,
And who's to say where
The harvest shall stop?

AUTUMN MORNING

Frances Frost

Now the old barns limber
Their patched roofs in the sun;
The deer drift in the timber;
The crows fly by one by one
Above the frosted orchard;
The narrow meadow stream
Is hushed and white, enfolded
In ice as in a dream.

OCTOBER

Rose Fyleman

The summer is over,
    The trees are all bare,
There is mist in the garden
    And frost in the air.
The meadows are empty
    And gathered the sheaves —
But isn't it lovely
    Kicking up leaves!

John from the garden
    Has taken the chairs;

It's dark in the evening
   And cold on the stairs.
Winter is coming
   And everyone grieves —
But isn't it lovely
   Kicking up leaves!

THEME IN YELLOW

Carl Sandburg

I spot the hills
With yellow balls in autumn.
I light the prairie cornfields
Orange and tawny gold clusters
And I am called pumpkins.
On the last of October
When dusk is fallen
Children join hands
And circle round me
Singing ghost songs
And love to the harvest moon;
I am a jack-o'-lantern
With terrible teeth
And the children know
I am fooling.

OCTOBER'S PARTY

George Cooper

October gave a party;
   The leaves by hundreds came —
The Chestnuts, Oaks, and Maples,
   And leaves of every name.
The sunshine spread a carpet,
   And everything was grand,
Miss Weather led the dancing,
   Professor Wind the band.

The Chestnuts came in yellow,
   The Oaks in crimson dressed;
The lovely Misses Maple
   In scarlet looked their best;
All balanced to their partners,
   And gaily fluttered by;
The sight was like a rainbow
   New fallen from the sky.

Then, in the rustic hollow,
   At hide-and-seek they played,
The party closed at sundown,
   And everybody stayed.
Professor Wind played louder;
   They flew along the ground;
And then the party ended
   In jolly "hands around."

THE WITCH OF WILLOWBY WOOD

Rowena Bennett

There once was a witch of Willowby Wood,
and a weird wild witch was she, with hair that was snarled
and hands that were gnarled, and a kickety, rickety
knee. She could jump, they say,
to the moon and back, but this I never did see.
Now Willowby Wood was near Sassafras Swamp,
where there's never a road or rut. And there by the
singing witch-hazel bush the old woman builded
her hut. She builded with neither a hammer or shovel. She
kneaded, she rolled out, she baked
her brown hovel. For *all* witches' houses, I've oft heard
it said, are made of stick candy and fresh
gingerbread. But the shingles that shingled this old
witch's roof were lollipop shingles and hurricane-proof, too
hard to be pelted and melted by rain.
(Why this is important, I soon will explain.)
One day there came running to Sassafras Swamp a dark little
shadowy mouse. He was noted for being a scoundrel
and scamp. And he gnawed at the old woman's house where
the doorpost was weak and the doorpost was worn.
And when the witch scolded, he laughed her to scorn.
And when the witch chased him, he felt quite delighted. She
never could catch him for she was nearsighted. And so,
though she quibbled, he gnawed and he nibbled.
The witch said, "I won't have my house
take a tumble. I'll search in my magical book for a spell
I can weave and a charm I can mumble to get you

228

away from this nook. It will be a good warning to other
bad mice, who won't earn their bread
but go stealing a slice."
"Your charms cannot hurt," said the mouse, looking pert.
Well, she looked in her book and she
waved her right arm, and she said the most magical
things. Till the mouse, feeling strange,
looked about in alarm, and found he was growing some
wings. He flapped and he fluttered the longer she muttered.
"And now, my fine fellow,
you'd best be aloof," said the witch as he floundered
around. "You can't stay on earth and you
can't gnaw my roof. It's lollipop-hard and it's
hurricane-proof. So you'd better take off
from the ground. If you are wise, stay in the skies."
Then in went the woman of Willowby Wood,
in to her hearthstone and cat.
There she put her old volume up high on the shelf, and
fanned her hot face with her hat. Then she said,
"That is that! I have just made a BAT!"

BLUE SMOKE

Frances Frost

Beside the mountain roads, the men
Heap and burn the leaves again.
While the mountain dusks grow brief and cold,
The children scuffle through fallen gold,
Knowing that soon, some early dawn,
The peaks will be white and the leaves be gone.

HALLOWE'EN

Harry Behn

Tonight is the night
When dead leaves fly
Like witches on switches
Across the sky,
When elf and sprite
Flit through the night
On a moony sheen.

Tonight is the night
When leaves make a sound
Like a gnome in his home
Under the ground,
When spooks and trolls
Creep out of holes
Mossy and green.

Tonight is the night
When pumpkins stare
Through sheaves and leaves
Everywhere,
When ghoul and ghost
And goblin host
Dance round their queen.
It's Hallowe'en!

THE LAST LEAF

Harry Behn

A few leaves stay for a while on the trees
After their color begins to turn,
And no other leaves seem as gold as these
Not even the ones our bonfires burn
With golden flames in piles on the ground.

A few leaves stay so long that I found
The one last leaf on a tree in the snow,
And when a galloping wind came round
The edge of our house and started to blow
Snow dust to sparkles floating free.

When the wind ran away, almost with me,
And sunshine settles quiet and cold,
There, like a bird, still on the tree
Was that lonesome leaf, no longer gold
But curly and brown and dry and old.

FIRST THANKSGIVING OF ALL

Nancy Byrd Turner

Peace and Mercy and Jonathan,
And Patience (very small),
Stood by the table giving thanks
The first Thanksgiving of all.
There was very little for them to eat,
Nothing special and nothing sweet;
Only bread and a little broth,
And a bit of fruit
   (and no tablecloth) ;
But Peace and Mercy and Jonathan
And Patience, in a row,
Stood up and asked a blessing on
Thanksgiving, long ago.
Thankful they were their ship had come
Safely across the sea;
Thankful they were for hearth and home,
And kin and company;
They were glad of broth to go with their **bread,**
Glad their apples were round and red,
Glad of mayflowers they would bring
Out of the woods again next spring.
So Peace and Mercy and Jonathan,
And Patience (very small),
Stood up gratefully giving thanks
The first Thanksgiving of all.

NOVEMBER'S COME

Joseph C. Lincoln

Hey, you swelled-up turkey feller!
Struttin' round so big and proud,
Pretty quick I guess your beller
   Won't be goin' quite so loud.
Say, I'd run and hide, I bet you,
   And I'd leave off eatin' some,
Else the choppin'-block'll get you, —
   Don't you know November's come?

Don't you know that Grandma's makin'
   Loads of mince and pun'kin pies?
Don't you smell those goodies cookin'?
   Can't you see' em? Where's your eyes?
Tell that rooster there that's crowin',
   Cute folks now are keepin' mum;
They don't show how fat they're growin'
   When they know November's come.

'Member when you tried to lick me?
   Yes, you did, and hurt me too!
Thought 'twas big to chase and pick me, —
   Well, I'll soon be pickin' you.
Oh, I know you're big and hearty,
   So you needn't strut and drum, —
Better make your will out, smarty,
   'Cause, you know, November's come.

"Gobble! gobble!" oh, no matter!
  Pretty quick you'll change your tune;
You'll be dead and in a platter,
  And I'll gobble pretty soon.
'If I was you I'd stop my puffin',
  And I'd look most awful glum; —
Hope they give you lots of stuffin'!
  AIN'T you glad November's come?

PLYMOUTH ROCK

Olive Driver

What do they see
When they come from the villages of New England,
From the corn lands of Iowa,
From the southern plantations,
From the plains and the mountains and the valleys,
From the great cities;
What do they see,
When they behold this rock?

They see a small, worn boulder,
With the date, 1620, in crude carving —
A patched-up stone, cracked in the moving
To its position above normal tide-line;
Quite insignificant it seems,
Dwarfed by the great, stone canopy above it,
Contrasting strangely with the flow
Of modern traffic on the busy highway.

Some see a battered boulder —
Nothing more;
And look surprised, amused, or disappointed,
And turn away with shrugs of the shoulders
And jokes upon their lips.

But others stand in silent reverence,
And men sometimes remove their hats,
And women wipe their eyes,
And murmur softly,
In halting explanations to their children;
For, gazing on the broad sweep of the bay
Where an ancient ship once anchored
And Pilgrims gathered in the bleak December
On the first day of that long, bitter winter,
They think about the graves upon the hill,
Where the heroic bronze of Massasoit
Faces a shining sea;
They think of Governor Carver and of Bradford
And of that doughty fighting man, Miles Standish;
Of young John Alden, helplessly in love
With the fair Pilgrim maid, Priscilla Mullins.

For after all is said or left unsaid,
After the disappointment and the levity,
This is the rock!
Other rocks may be larger,
Or more impressive, or more beautiful;
Other rocks may not be scarred,
Or chipped or broken;
But, this is the rock!

This is the rock of vision,
To which a little group of dauntless souls
Set sail in a frail bark
To found a nation on an unknown shore.

This is the rock of faith,
That gave that gallant band the fortitude
To turn disaster, heartbreak and despair
Into the harvest and the first Thanksgiving.

This is the rock of freedom —
The precious, priceless liberty to choose
One's own religion, trade and way of life.

This is the rock
From which our country rose —
The rock to which our ship of state is anchored.

Whenever in our history
Men have dreamed and dared and pioneered,
Whenever men have fought and bled and died
For family, for country, for principle,
Behind them and beneath them is the shadow
of a plain, gray stone;
This is the rock!

Wherever in our land
The white steeples of country meeting houses
And the dark towers of city churches

Rise up against the sky;
Wherever free enterprises and colleges
Foster the pursuits of a free people;
There is the shadow of the MAYFLOWER
Riding at anchor in Plymouth harbor,
And a small, gray boulder
On a barren shore;
This is the rock!

IT SIFTS FROM LEADEN SIEVES

Emily Dickinson

It sifts from leaden sieves,
It powders all the wood,
It fills with alabaster wool
The wrinkles of the road.

It makes an even face
Of mountain and of plain, —
Unbroken forehead from the east
Unto the east again.

It reaches to the fence,
It wraps it, rail by rail,
Till it is lost in fleeces;
It flings a crystal veil

On stump and stack and stem, —
The summer's empty room,
Acres of seams where harvests were,
Recordless, but for them.

It ruffles wrists of posts,
As ankles of a queen, —
Then stills its artisans like ghosts,
Denying they have been.

WINTER NOON

Sara Teasdale

Snow-dust driven over the snow
In glittering light,
Low hills, far as the eye can go,
White on white;
Blue as a blue jay, shadows run
Due north from every tree —
Chipmunk, do you like the sun,
The blowing snow and me?

VILLAGE CHRISTMAS

Margaret Widdemer

As I went down the village street
   The wind blew glittering and light
And one last church-bell quivered sweet
   And wreath-hung doors stood kind and bright

And past the hedge-lines' ruffs of snow
   As by each little house I came
Like rosy tulip-buds arow
   I saw the window candles flame,

And round a silver shining tree
   Between the starlight and the snow
Our children all sang merrily
   How Christ and joy were here below:

And Christ was there and joy was there:
   Still we could love, and still believe.
I bent my head and said my prayer;
   "I thank You, Lord, for Christmas Eve."

CHRISTMAS MORNING

Elizabeth Madox Roberts

If Bethlehem were here today,
Or this were very long ago,
There wouldn't be a winter time
Nor any cold or snow.

I'd run out through the garden gate,
And down along the pasture walk;
And off beside the cattle barns
I'd hear a kind of gentle talk.

I'd move the heavy iron chain
And pull away the wooden pin;
I'd push the door a little bit
And tiptoe very softly in.

The pigeons and the yellow hens
And all the cows would stand away;
Their eyes would open wide to see
A lady in the manger hay,
If this were very long ago
And Bethlehem were here today.

And mother held my hand and smiled —
I mean the lady would — and she
Would take the wooly blankets off
Her little boy so I could see.

His shut-up eyes would be asleep,
And he would look like our John,
And he would be all crumpled too,
And have a pinkish color on.

I'd watch his breath go in and out.
His little clothes would all be white.
I'd slip my fingers in his hand
To feel how he could hold it tight.

And she would smile and say, "Take care,"
The mother, Mary, would "Take care;"
And I would kiss his little hand
And touch his hair.

While Mary put the blankets back
The gentle talk would soon begin.
And when I'd tiptoe softly out
I'd meet the wise men going in.

A VISIT FROM ST. NICHOLAS

Clement Clarke Moore

'Twas the night before Christmas, when all through the house
Not a creature was stirring, not even a mouse;
The stockings were hung by the chimney with care,
In hopes that St. Nicholas soon would be there;
The children were nestled all snug in their beds,
While visions of sugar-plums danced in their heads;
And mamma in her 'kerchief, and I in my cap,
Had just settled our brains for a long winter's nap,
When out on the lawn there arose such a clatter,
I sprang from the bed to see what was the matter.
Away to the window I flew like a flash,
Tore open the shutters and threw up the sash.
The moon on the breast of the new-fallen snow
Gave the luster of mid-day to objects below,
When, what to my wondering eyes should appear,
But a miniature sleigh, and eight tiny reindeer,
With a little old driver, so lively and quick,
I knew in a moment it must be St. Nick.
More rapid than eagles his coursers they came,
And he whistled, and shouted, and called them by name:
"Now, *Dasher!* now, *Dancer!* now, *Prancer* and *Vixen!*
On, *Comet!* on, *Cupid!* on, *Donder* and *Blitzen!*
To the top of the porch! to the top of the wall!
Now dash away! dash away! dash away all!"
As dry leaves that before the wild hurricane fly,
When they meet with an obstacle, mount to the sky,
So up to the house-top the coursers they flew,

With the sleigh full of toys, and St. Nicholas too.
And then, in a twinkling, I heard on the roof
The prancing and pawing of each little hoof.
As I drew in my head, and was turning around,
Down the chimney St. Nicholas came with a bound.
He was dressed all in fur, from his head to his foot,
And his clothes were all tarnished with ashes and soot;
A bundle of toys he had flung on his back,
And he looked like a peddler just opening his pack.
His eyes — how they twinkled! his dimples how merry!
His cheeks were like roses, his nose like a cherry!
His droll little mouth was drawn up like a bow,
And the beard of his chin was as white as the snow;
The stump of a pipe he held tight in his teeth,
And the smoke it encircled his head like a wreath;
He had a broad face and a little round belly,
That shook, when he laughed, like a bowlful of jelly.
He was chubby and plump, a right jolly old elf,
And I laughed when I saw him, in spite of myself;
A wink of his eye and a twist of his head,
Soon gave me to know I had nothing to dread;
He spoke not a word, but went straight to his work,
And filled all the stockings; then turned with a jerk,
And laying his finger aside of his nose,
And giving a nod, up the chimney he rose;
He sprang to his sleigh, to his team gave a whistle,
And away they all flew like the down of a thistle.
But I heard him exclaim, ere he drove out of sight,
"Happy Christmas to all, and to all a good night."

CHRISTMAS IN THE HEART

Unknown

It is Christmas in the mansion,
　　Yule-log fires and silken frocks;
It is Christmas in the cottage,
　　Mother's filling little socks.

It is Christmas on the highway,
　　In the thronging, busy mart;
But the dearest, truest Christmas
　　Is the Christmas in the heart.

CHRISTMAS BELLS

Henry Wadsworth Longfellow

I heard the bells on Christmas Day
Their old, familiar carols play,
　　And wild and sweet
　　The words repeat
Of peace on earth, goodwill to men!

And thought how, as the day had come,
The belfries of all Christendom
　　Had rolled along
　　The unbroken song
Of peace on earth, goodwill to men!

Till, ringing, singing on its way,
The world received from night to day,
   A voice, a chime,
   A chant sublime
Of peace on earth, goodwill to men!

Then from each black, accursed mouth
The cannon thundered in the South,
   And with the sound
   The carols drowned
Of peace on earth, goodwill to men!

It was as if an earthquake rent
The hearth-stones of a continent,
   And made forlorn
   The households born
Of peace on earth, goodwill to men!

And in despair I bowed my head;
"There is no peace on earth," I said;
   "For hate is strong,
   And mocks the song
Of peace on earth, goodwill to men!

Then pealed the bells more loud and deep:
"God is not dead; nor doth He sleep!
   The Wrong shall fail,
   The Right prevail,
With peace on earth, goodwill to men!"

CHRISTMAS CAROL

Old Rhyme

God bless the master of this house,
    The mistress also,
And all the little children,
    That round the table go,
And all your kin and kinsmen
    That dwell both far and near;
I wish you a Merry Christmas
    And a Happy New Year.

TAKING DOWN THE TREE

Aileen Fisher

It's over, it's over!
A new year is here.
It's over, white angel,
you'll sleep for a year;
all wrapped up in tissue
and hidden away,
for Christmas is over . . .
I wish it could stay!

It's over, bright tinsel,
it's over, bright star.
Oh, bare little fir tree
how sober you are.
We waited for Christmas
so long, and at last
it came . . . but it's over,
it's over so fast.

It's over, it's over!
The crèche must come down,
the Child in the manger
in Bethlehem town,
and Mary and Joseph,
the sheep and the ox,
the shepherds and wise men —
they fill a whole box.

It's over . . . the singing,
the candles aglow,
the wreaths and the holly,
the lights on the snow.
The magic is over
that filled Christmastide,
but oh, we can keep it
still shining inside!

In Praise of People

THE BAILIFF'S DAUGHTER
OF ISLINGTON

Unknown

There was a youth, and a well-loved youth,
    And he was a squire's son,
He loved the bailiff's daughter dear,
    That lived in Islington.

Yet she was coy and would not believe
    That he did love her so,
And not at any time would she
    A favor to him show.

But when his friends did understand
    His fond and foolish mind,
They sent him up to London
    An apprentice for to bind.

And when he had been seven long years,
    And never his love could see —
"Many a tear have I shed for her sake,
    When she little thought of me."

Then all the maids of Islington
    Went forth to sport and play,
All but the bailiff's daughter dear;
    She secretly stole away.

She pulled off her gown of green,
   And put on ragged attire,
And to fair London she would go
   Her true love to inquire.

And as she went along the high road,
   The weather being hot and dry,
She sat her down upon a green bank,
   And her true love came riding by.

She started up, with color so red,
   Catching hold of his bridle rein;
"One penny, one penny, kind sir," she said,
   Will ease me of much pain."

"Before I give you one penny, sweetheart,
   Pray tell me where you were born,"
"At Islington, kind sir," said she,
   "Where I have had many a scorn."

"I pray thee, sweetheart, then tell to me
   O tell me, whether you know
The bailiff's daughter of Islington."
   "She is dead, sir, long ago."

"If she be dead, then take my horse,
   My saddle and bridle also;
For I will into some far country,
   Where no man shall me know."

"O stay, O stay, thou goodly youth,
    She standeth by thy side;
She is here alive, she is not dead,
    And ready to be thy bride."

"O farewell grief, and welcome joy,
    Ten thousand times therefore;
For now I have found my own true love,
    Whom I thought I should never see more."

LITTLE JOHN BOTTLEJOHN

Laura E. Richards

Little John Bottlejohn lived on the hill,
    And a blithe little man was he.
And he won the heart of a pretty mermaid
    Who lived in the deep blue sea.
And every evening she used to sit
    And sing by the rocks of the sea,
"O, little John Bottlejohn, pretty John Bottlejohn,
    Won't you come out to me?"

Little John Bottlejohn heard her song,
    And he opened his little door,
And he hopped and he skipped, and he skipped and he hopped,
    Until he came down to the shore.
And there on the rocks sat the little mermaid,
    And still she was singing so free,

"Oh, little John Bottlejohn, pretty John Bottlejohn,
   Won't you come out to me?"

Little John Bottlejohn made a bow,
   And the mermaid, she made one too;
And she said, "Oh, I never saw anyone half
   So perfectly sweet as you!
In my lovely home 'neath the ocean foam,
   How happy we both might be!
Oh! little John Bottlejohn, pretty John Bottlejohn,
   Won't you come down with me?"

Little John Bottlejohn said, "Oh yes!
   I'll willingly go with you,
And I never shall quail at the sight of your tail,
   For perhaps I may grow one too."
So he took her hand, and he left the land,
   And plunged in the foaming main.
And little John Bottlejohn, pretty John Bottlejohn,
   Never was seen again.

THE BIG TENT UNDER THE ROOF

Ogden Nash

     Noises new to sea and land
     Issue from the circus band.
     Each musician looks like mumps
     From blowing umpah umpah umps.

Lovely girls in spangled pants
Ride on gilded elephants.
Elephants are useful friends,
They have handles on both ends;
They hold each other's hindmost handles
And flee from mice and Roman candles.
Their hearts are gold, their hides are emery,
And they have a most tenacious memory.

Notice also, girls and boys,
The circus horses' avoirdupois.
Far and wide the wily scouts
Seek these snow-white stylish stouts.
Calmer steeds were never found
Unattached to a merry-go-round.
Equestriennes prefer to jump
Onto horses pillow-plump.

Equestriennes will never ride
As other people do, astride.
They like to balance on one foot,
And wherever they get, they won't stay put.
They utter frequent whoops and yips,
And have the most amazing hips.
Pink seems to be their favorite color,
And very few things are very much duller.

Yet I for one am more than willing
That everything should be less thrilling.
My heart and lungs both bound and balk

When high-wire walkers start to walk.
They ought to perish, yet they don't;
Some fear they will, some fear they won't.

I lack the adjectives, verbs and nouns
To do full justice to the clowns.
Their hearts are constantly breaking, I hear,
And who am I to interfere?
I'd rather shake hands with Mr. Ringling
And tell him his circus is a beautiful thingling.

THE COXSWAIN'S LINE

Lt. H. E. Cressman, U.S.N.

This is the story the Coxswain told
To a bunch of boots in the forward hold.

Shanghaied by a whaler I worked as a sailor,
    And fetched up in old Bombay;
After six weeks afloat in an old whaleboat,
    That steered like a stack of hay.

I know the shores of the lonely Azores
    And the lights of Sidney Head;
Where we lay close hauled and the leadsman called
    The depth of the channel's bed.

I've been through the Straits and the Golden Gates,
    Mined diamonds for months by the Karat;
I've been in Algiers, stayed in London for years,
    And climbed to the top of Mt. Ararat.

I've sailed a ship in the hurricane's grip,
    And a rotten old tub was she;
Where we saved our hides and little besides
    From a wreck in the old North Sea.

I've seen the Soudan and the heart of Japan,
    And I've speckled the Indian Seas,
I've travelled the Highlands; been all through the Islands
    And froze in the bleak Pyrenees.

I've been Captain and crew and Bos'n too,
    Sailed round the Horn thirty times,
On a ship that was built like a crazy quilt,
    With a cargo of liquor and limes.

I served in the Corps in the late Spanish war,
    And never once had a rest.
I was shot in the spine and dropped out of line
    And died with a ball in my chest.

        This is the story the Coxswain told
        To a bunch of boots in the forward hold.

THOMAS JEFFERSON

Stephen Vincent Benét

Thomas Jefferson,
What do you say
Under the gravestone
Hidden away?

"I was a giver,
I was a molder,
I was a builder
With a strong shoulder."

Six feet and over,
Large-boned and ruddy,
The eyes grey-hazel
But bright with study.

The big hands clever
With pen and fiddle
And ready, ever,
For any riddle.

From buying empires
To planting 'taters,
From Declarations
To trick dumb-waiters.

"I liked the people,
The sweat and crowd of them,
Trusted them always
And spoke aloud of them.

"I liked all learning
And wished to share it
Abroad like pollen
For all who merit.

"I liked fine houses
With Greek pilasters,
And built them surely,
My touch a master's.

"I liked queer gadgets
And secret shelves,
And helping nations
To rule themselves.

"Jealous of others?
Not always candid?
But huge of vision
And open-handed.

"A wild-goose chaser?
Now and again,
Build Monticello,
You little men!

"Design my plow, sirs,
They use it still,
Or found my college
At Charlottesville.

"And still go questing
New things and thinkers,
And keep as busy
As twenty tinkers.

"While always guarding
The people's freedom —
You need more hands, sir?
I didn't need 'em.

"They call you rascal?
They called me worse.
You'd do grand things, sir,
But lack the purse?

"I got no riches.
I died a debtor.
I died free-hearted
And that was better.

"For life was freakish
But life was fervent,
And I was always
Life's willing servant.

"Life, life's too weighty?
Too long a haul, sir?
I lived past eighty.
I liked it all, sir."

LAMENT FOR THE ALAMO

Arthur Guiterman

Davy Crockett in his woodman dress,
    His shirt of the hide of a yearling doe
And his coonskin cap and his rifle, Bess —
    Dead he lies in the Alamo.

Ned the Bee-hunter with the coal-black curls,
    Straight as a spear shaft, lithe as a bow,
With a song for the world and a laugh for the girls —
    Dead he lies in the Alamo.

Colonel Bowie of the twelve-inch blade,
    Gentle of speech and sure of blow,
Prone on the heap that his sword arm made —
    Dead he lies in the Alamo.

Stout were their hearts the red week long
    That they strove with the hordes of Mexico,
But their powder failed and the odds were strong —
    Dead they lie in the Alamo.

Back to back in the slaughter pen,
    Steel to the steel of a ruthless foe,
Travis fell with his nine-score men —
    Dead they lie in the Alamo.

Gone from the wood and the waterside,
    Gone from the haunts of the buffalo,
They ride no more where they loved to ride —
    Dead they lie in the Alamo.

Texans, plainsmen, pioneers,
    Pay the debt that your rifles owe:
Pay your debt of blood and tears
    For those who died in the Alamo!

REMEMBER THE ALAMO!

THE CAPTAIN STOOD ON
THE CARRONADE

Frederick Marryat

The Captain stood on the Carronade — "First lieutenant,"
    says he,
"Send all my merry men aft here, for they must list to me:
I haven't the gift of the gab, my sons, because I'm bred to
    the sea;

That ship there is a Frenchman, who means to fight with we.
    Odds blood, hammer and tongs, long as I've
      been to sea,
    I've fought 'gainst every odds — but I've gained
    the victory!

"That ship there is a Frenchman, and if we don't take she,
'Tis a thousand bullets to one, that she will capture we;
I haven't the gift of the gab, my boys; so each man to his
  gun;
If she's not mine in half an hour, I'll flog each mother's son.
    Odds bobs, hammer and tongs, long as I've
      been to sea,
    I've fought 'gainst every odds — and I've
    gained the victory."

We fought for twenty minutes, when the Frenchman had
  enough;
"I little thought," said he, "that you men were of such stuff."
The Captain took the Frenchman's sword, a low bow made
  to he;
"I haven't the gift of the gab, Monsieur, but polite I wish to
  be.
    Odds bobs, hammer and tongs, long as I've
      been to sea,
    I've fought 'gainst every odds — and I've
    gained the victory."

262

Our Captain sent for all of us: "My merry men," said he,
"I haven't the gift of the gab, my lads, but yet I thankful be;
You've done our duty handsomely, each man stood to his
gun;
If you hadn't, you villains, as sure as day, I'd have flogged
each mother's son!
    Odds bobs, hammer and tongs, as long as I'm
      at sea,
    I'll fight 'gainst every odds — and I'll gain the
      victory."

THE GREATEST CITY

Walt Whitman

What do you think endures?
Do you think the greatest city endures?
Or a teeming manufacturing state? or a prepared
constitution? or the best built steamships?
Or hotels of granite and iron? or any chef-d'oeuvres of
engineering, forts, armaments?
Away! These are not to be cherished for themselves,
They fill their hour, the dancers dance, the musicians play
for them,
The show passes, all does well enough of course,
All does very well till one flash of defiance.

The greatest city is that which has the greatest men or women,
If it be a few ragged huts, it is still the greatest city in
the whole world.

THE ENCHANTED SHIRT

John Hay

I

The King was sick. His cheek was red,
  And his eye was clear and bright;
He ate and drank with a kingly zest,
  And peacefully snored at night.

But he said he was sick, and a king should know,
  And doctors came by the score.
They did not cure him. He cut off their heads,
  And sent to the schools for more.

At last two famous doctors came,
  And one was as poor as a rat, —
He had passed his life in studious toil,
  And never found time to grow fat.

The other had never looked in a book;
  His patients gave him no trouble:
If they recovered, they paid him well;
  If they died, their heirs paid double.

Together they looked at the royal tongue,
  As the King on his couch reclined;
In succession they thumped his august chest,
  But no trace of disease could find.

The old sage said, "You're as sound as a nut."
  "Hang him up," roared the King in a gale —
In a ten-knot gale of royal rage!
  The other leech grew a shade pale;

But he pensively rubbed his sagacious nose,
  And thus his prescription ran —
The King will be well, if he sleeps one night
  In the Shirt of a Happy Man.

II

Wide o'er the realm the couriers rode,
  And fast their horses ran,
And many they saw, and to many they spoke,
  But they found no Happy Man.

They found poor men who would fain be rich,
  And rich who thought they were poor;
And men who twisted their waist in stays,
  And women that short hose wore.

They saw two men by the roadside sit,
  And both bemoaned their lot;
For one had buried his wife, he said,
  And the other one had not.

At last they came to a village gate,
  A beggar lay whistling there;

He whistled, and sang, and laughed, and rolled
    On the grass in the soft June air.

The weary courtiers paused and looked
    At the scamp so blithe and gay;
And one of them said, "Heaven save you, friend
    You seem to be happy to-day."

"Oh yes, fair sirs," the rascal laughed,
    And his voice rang free and glad;
"An idle man has so much to do
    That he never has time to be sad."

"This is our man," the courier said;
    "Our luck has led us aright.
I will give you a hundred ducats, friend,
    For the loan of your shirt to-night."

The merry blackguard lay back on the grass,
    And laughed till his face was black;
"I would do it, God wot," and he roared with the fun,
    "But I haven't a shirt to my back."

III

Each day to the King the reports came in
    Of his unsuccessful spies,
And the sad panorama of human woes
    Passed daily under his eyes.

266

And he grew ashamed of his useless life,
   And his maladies hatched in gloom;
He opened his windows and let the air
   Of the free heaven into his room.

And out he went in the world, and toiled
   In his own appointed way;
And the people blessed him, the land was glad,
   And the King was well and gay.

THE GIFT OUTRIGHT

Robert Frost

The land was ours before we were the land's.
She was our land more than a hundred years
Before we were her people. She was ours
In Massachusetts, in Virginia,
But we were England's, still colonials,
Possessing what we still were unpossessed by,
Possessed by what we now no more possessed.
Something we were withholding made us weak
Until we found out that it was ourselves
We were withholding from our land of living,
And forthwith found salvation in surrender.
Such as we were we gave ourselves outright
(The deed of gift was many deeds of war)
To the land vaguely realizing westward,
But still unstoried, artless, unenhanced,
Such as she was, such as she would become.

IN THE DAYS WHEN THE CATTLE RAN

Hamlin Garland

It was worth the while of a boy to live
In the days when the prairie lay wide to the herds,
When the sod had a hundred joys to give
And the wind had a thousand words.
　　It was well to be led
　　Where the wild horses fed
As free as the swarming birds.

Not yet had the plough and the sickle swept
The lily from meadow, the roses from hill,
Not yet had the horses been haltered and kept
In stalls and sties at a master's will.
　　With eyes wild-blazing,
　　Or drowsily grazing,
They wandered untouched by the thill.

And the boy! With torn hat flaring,
With sturdy red legs which the thick brambles tore,
As wild as the colts, he went faring and sharing
The grasses and fruits which the brown soil bore.
　　Treading softly for fear
　　Of the snake ever near,
Unawed by the lightning or black tempest's roar.

268

But out on the prairie the ploughs crept together,
The meadow turned black at stroke of the share,
The shaggy colts yielded to clutch of the tether,
The red lilies died, and the vines ceased to bear.
     And nothing was left to the boys
     But the dim remembrance of joys
     When the swift cattle ran,
     Unhindered of man,
And their herders were free as the clouds in the air.

THE COPPERFACES

Carl Sandburg

The copperfaces, the red men, handed us tobacco,
the weed for the pipe of friendship,
also the bah-tah-to, the potato, the spud.
Sunflowers came from Peruvians in ponchos.
Early Italians taught us of chestnuts,
walnuts and peaches being Persian mementoes,
Siberians finding for us what rye might do,
Hindus coming through with the cucumber,
Egyptians giving us the onion, the pea,
Arabians handing advice with one gift:
"Some like it, some say it's just spinach."
     To the Chinese we have given
     kerosene, bullets, bibles
and they have given us radishes, soybeans, silk,
poems, paintings, proverbs, porcelain, egg foo yong,
gunpowder, Fourth of July firecrackers, fireworks,

and labor gangs for the first Pacific railways.
    Now we may thank these people
    or reserve our thanks
    and speak of them as outsiders
    and imply the request,
"Would you just as soon get off the earth?"
holding ourselves aloof in pride of distinction
saying to ourselves this costs us nothing
as though hate has no cost
as though hate ever grew anything worth growing.
Yes we may say this trash is beneath our notice
or we may hold them in respect and affection
as fellow creepers on a commodious planet
saying, "Yes you too you too are people."

THEY HAVE YARNS

Carl Sandburg

            They have yarns
    Of a skyscraper so tall they had to put hinges
    On the two top stories so to let the moon go by,
    Of one corn crop in Missouri when the roots
    Went so deep and drew off so much water
    The Mississippi riverbed that year was dry,
    Of pancakes so thin they had only one side,
Of "a fog so thick we shingled the barn and six feet out on
    the fog,"
Of Pecos Pete straddling a cyclone in Texas and riding it to

the west coast where "it rained out under him,"

Of the man who drove a swarm of bees across the Rocky
Mountains and the Desert "and didn't lose a bee,"

Of a mountain railroad curve where the engineer in his cab
can touch the caboose and spit in the conductor's eye,

Of the boy who climbed a cornstalk growing so fast he would
have starved to death if they hadn't shot biscuits up to
him,

Of the old man's whiskers: "When the wind was with him
his whiskers arrived a day before he did,"

Of the hen laying a square egg and cackling, "Ouch!" and of
hens laying eggs with the dates printed on them,

Of the ship captain's shadow: it froze to the deck one cold
winter night,

Of mutineers on that same ship put to chipping rust with
rubber hammers,

Of the sheep counter who was fast and accurate: "I just
count their feet and divide by four,"

Of the man so tall he must climb a ladder to shave himself,

Of the runt so teeny-weeny it takes two men and a boy to
see him,

Of mosquitoes: one can kill a dog, two of them a man,

Of a cyclone that sucked cookstoves out of the kitchen, up
the chimney flue, and on to the next town,

Of the same cyclone picking up wagon-tracks in Nebraska
and dropping them over in the Dakotas,

Of the hook-and-eye snake unlocking itself into forty pieces,
each piece two inches long, then in nine seconds flat
snapping itself together again,

Of the watch swallowed by the cow — when they butchered
her a year later the watch was running and had the cor-
rect time,

271

Of horned snakes, hoop snakes that roll themselves where
they want to go, and rattlesnakes carrying bells instead of
rattles on their tails,

Of the herd of cattle in California getting lost in a giant red-
wood tree that had hollowed out,

Of the man who killed a snake by putting its tail in its mouth
so it swallowed itself,

Of railroad trains whizzing along so fast they reach the sta-
tion before the whistle,

Of pigs so thin the farmer had to tie knots in their tails to
keep them from crawling through the cracks in their pens,

Of Paul Bunyan's big blue ox, Babe, measuring between the
eyes forty-two ax-handles and a plug of Star tobacco exactly,

Of John Henry's hammer and curve of its swing and his
singing of it as "a rainbow round my shoulder."

HIAWATHA'S CHILDHOOD

Henry Wadsworth Longfellow

FROM THE SONG OF HIAWATHA

By the shores of Gitche Gumee,
By the shining Big-Sea-Water,
Stood the wigwam of Nokomis,
Daughter of the Moon, Nokomis.
Dark behind it rose the forest,
Rose the black and gloomy pine-trees,
Rose the firs with cones upon them;
Bright before it beat the water,
Beat the clear and sunny water,

Beat the shining Big-Sea-Water.

There the wrinkled, old Nokomis
Nursed the little Hiawatha,
Rocked him in his linden cradle,
Bedded soft in moss and rushes,
Safely bound with reindeer sinews;
Stilled his fretful wail by saying,
"Hush! the Naked Bear will get thee!"
Lulled him into slumber, singing,
"Ewa-yea! my little owlet!
Who is this, that lights the wigwam?
With his great eyes lights the wigwam?
Ewa-yea! my little owlet!"

Many things Nokomis taught him
Of the stars that shine in heaven;
Showed him Ishkoodah, the comet,
Ishkoodah, with fiery tresses;
Showed the Death-Dance of the spirits,
Warriors with their plumes and war-clubs,
Flaring far away to northward
In the frosty nights of Winter;
Showed the broad, white road in heaven,
Pathway of the ghosts, the shadows,
Running straight across the heavens,
Crowded with the ghosts, the shadows.

At the door on summer evenings
Sat the little Hiawatha;
Heard the whispering of the pine-trees,
Heard the lapping of the waters,
Sounds of music, words of wonder;
"Minne-wawa!" said the pine-trees,
"Mudway-aushka!" said the water.

Saw the fire-fly, Wah-wah-taysee,
Flitting through the dusk of evening,
With the twinkle of its candle
Lighting up the brakes and bushes,
And he sang the song of children,
Sang the song Nokomis taught him;
"Wah-wah-taysee, little fire-fly,
Little, flitting, white-fire insect,
Little, dancing, white-fire creature,
Light me with your little candle,
Ere upon my bed I lay me,
Ere in sleep I close my eyelids!"
  Saw the moon rise from the water
Rippling, rounding from the water,
Saw the flecks and shadows on it,
Whispered, "What is that, Nokomis?"
And the good Nokomis answered:
"Once a warrior, very angry,
Seized his grandmother, and threw her
Up into the sky at midnight;
Right against the moon he threw her;
'Tis her body that you see there."
  Saw the rainbow in the heaven,
In the eastern sky, the rainbow,
Whispered, "What is that, Nokomis?"
And the good Nokomis answered:
" 'Tis the heaven of flowers you see there;
All the wild flowers of the forest,
All the lilies of the prairie,
When on earth they fade and perish,
Blossom in that heaven above us."
  When he heard the owls at midnight,

Hooting, laughing in the forest,
"What is that?" he cried in terror;
"What is that?" he said, "Nokomis?"
And the good Nokomis answered:
"That is but the owl and owlet,
Talking in their native language,
Talking, scolding at each other."
   Then the little Hiawatha
Learned of every bird its language,
Learned their names and all their secrets,
How they built their nests in Summer,
Where they hid themselves in Winter,
Talked with them whene'er he met them,
Called them "Hiawatha's Chickens."
   Of all beasts he learned the language,
Learned their names and all their secrets,
How the beavers built their lodges,
Where the squirrels hid their acorns,
How the reindeer ran so swiftly,
Why the rabbit was so timid,
Talked with them whene'er he met them,
Called them "Hiawatha's Brothers."
   Then Iagoo, the great boaster,
He the marvelous story-teller,
He the traveler and the talker,
He the friend of old Nokomis,
Made a bow for Hiawatha:
From a branch of ash he made it,
From an oak-bough made the arrows,
Tipped with flint, and winged with feathers,
And the cord he made of deer-skin.
   Then he said to Hiawatha:

"Go, my son, into the forest,
Where the red deer herd together,
Kill for us a famous roebuck,
Kill for us a deer with antlers!"
Forth into the forest straightway
All alone walked Hiawatha
Proudly, with his bow and arrows;
And the birds sang round him, o'er him,
"Do not shoot us, Hiawatha!"
Sang the Opechee, the robin,
Sang the bluebird, the Owaissa,
"Do not shoot us, Hiawatha!"
Up the oak-tree, close beside him,
Sprang the squirrel, Adjidaumo,
In and out among the branches,
Coughed and chattered from the oak-tree,
Laughed, and said between his laughing,
"Do not shoot me, Hiawatha!"
And the rabbit from his pathway
Leaped aside, and at a distance
Sat erect upon his haunches,
Half in fear and half in frolic,
Saying to the little hunter,
"Do not shoot me, Hiawatha!"
But he heeded not, nor heard them,
For his thoughts were with the red deer;
On their tracks his eyes were fastened,
Leading downward to the river,
To the ford across the river,
And as one in slumber walked he.
Hidden in the alder-bushes,
There he waited till the deer came,

Till he saw two antlers lifted,
Saw two eyes look from the thicket,
Saw two nostrils point to windward,
And a deer came down the pathway,
Flecked with leafy light and shadow.
And his heart within him fluttered,
Trembled like the leaves above him,
Like the birch-leaf palpitated,
As the deer came down the pathway.
    Then, upon one knee uprising,
Hiawatha aimed an arrow;
Scarce a twig moved with his motion,
Scarce a leaf was stirred or rustled,
But the wary roebuck started,
Stamped with all his hoofs together,
Listened with one foot uplifted,
Leaped as if to meet the arrow;
Ah! the singing, fatal arrow,
Like a wasp it buzzed and stung him!
    Dead he lay there in the forest,
By the ford across the river;
Beat his timid heart no longer,
But the heart of Hiawatha
Throbbed and shouted and exulted,
As he bore the red deer homeward,
And Iagoo and Nokomis
Hailed his coming with applauses.
    From the red deer's hide Nokomis
Made a cloak for Hiawatha,
From the red deer's flesh Nokomis
Made a banquet to his honor.
All the village came and feasted,

All the guests praised Hiawatha,
Called him Strong-Heart, Soan-ge-taha!
Called him Loon-Heart, Mahn-go-taysee!

PAUL REVERE'S RIDE

Henry Wadsworth Longfellow

Listen, my children, and you shall hear
Of the midnight ride of Paul Revere,
On the eighteenth of April, in Seventy-five;
Hardly a man is now alive
Who remembers that famous day and year.

He said to his friend, "If the British march
By land or sea from the town tonight,
Hang a lantern aloft in the belfry arch
Of the North Church tower as a signal light, —
One, if by land, and two, if by sea;
And I on the opposite shore will be,
Ready to ride and spread the alarm
Through every Middlesex village and farm,
For the country folk to be up and to arm."

Then he said, "Good night!" and with muffled oar
Silently rowed to the Charlestown shore,
Just as the moon rose over the bay,
Where swinging wide at her moorings lay

The *Somerset*, British man-of-war;
A phantom ship, with each mast and spar
Across the moon like a prison bar,
And a huge black hulk, that was magnified
By its own reflection in the tide.

Meanwhile, his friend, through alley and street,
Wanders and watches with eager ears,
Till in the silence around him he hears
The muster of men at the barrack door,
The sound of arms, and the tramp of feet,
And the measured tread of the grenadiers,
Marching down to their boats on the shore.

Then he climbed the tower of the Old North Church,
By the wooden stairs, with stealthy tread,
To the belfry chamber overhead,
And startled the pigeons from their perch
On the somber rafters, that round him made
Masses and moving shapes of shade, —
By the trembling ladder, steep and tall,
To the highest window in the wall,
Where he paused to listen and look down
A moment on the roofs of the town,
And the moonlight flowing over all.

Beneath, in the churchyard, lay the dead,
In their night encampment on the hill,
Wrapped in silence so deep and still
That he could hear, like a sentinel's tread,

The watchful night wind, as it went
Creeping along from tent to tent,
And seeming to whisper, "All is well!"
A moment only he feels the spell
Of the place and the hour, and the secret dread
Of the lonely belfry and the dead;
For suddenly all his thoughts are bent
On a shadowy something far away,
Where the river widens to meet the bay, —
A line of black that bends and floats
On the rising tide, like a bridge of boats.

Meanwhile, impatient to mount and ride,
Booted and spurred, with a heavy stride
On the opposite shore walked Paul Revere.
Now he patted his horse's side,
Now gazed at the landscape far and near,
Then, impetuous, stamped the earth,
And turned and tightened his saddle girth;
But mostly he watched with eager search
The belfry tower of the Old North Church,
As it rose above the graves on the hill,
Lonely and spectral and somber and still.
And lo! as he looks, on the belfry's height
A glimmer, and then a gleam of light!
He springs to the saddle, the bridle he turns,
But lingers and gazes, till full on his sight,
A second lamp in the belfry burns!

A hurry of hoofs in a village street,
A shape in the moonlight, a bulk in the dark,

And beneath, from the pebbles, in passing, a spark
Struck out by a steed flying fearless and fleet!
That was all! And yet, through the gloom and the light,
The fate of a nation was riding that night;
And the spark struck out by that steed, in his flight,
Kindled the land into flame with its heat.

He has left the village and mounted the steep,
And beneath him, tranquil and broad and deep,
Is the Mystic, meeting the ocean tides;
And under the alders that skirt its edge,
Now soft on the sand, now loud on the ledge,
Is heard the tramp of his steed as he rides.

It was twelve by the village clock,
When he crossed the bridge into Medford town.
He heard the crowing of the cock,
And the barking of the farmer's dog,
And felt the damp of the river fog,
That rises after the sun goes down.

It was one by the village clock,
When he galloped into Lexington.
He saw the gilded weathercock
Swim in the moonlight as he passed,
And the meeting-house windows, blank and bare,
Gaze at him with a spectral glare,
As if they already stood aghast
At the bloody work they would look upon.

It was two by the village clock,
When he came to the bridge in Concord town.
He heard the bleating of the flock,
And the twitter of birds among the trees,
And felt the breath of the morning breeze
Blowing over the meadows brown.
And one was safe and asleep in his bed
Who at the bridge would be first to fall,
Who that day would be lying dead,
Pierced by a British musket ball.

You know the rest. In the books you have read
How the British Regulars fired and fled, —
How the farmers gave them ball for ball,
From behind each fence and farmyard wall,
Chasing the redcoats down the lane,
Then crossing the fields to emerge again
Under the trees at the turn of the road,
And only pausing to fire and load.

So through the night rode Paul Revere;
And so through the night went his cry of alarm
To every Middlesex village and farm, —
A cry of defiance and not of fear,
A voice in the darkness, a knock at the door,
And a word that shall echo forevermore!
For, borne on the night wind of the Past,
Through all our history, to the last,
In the hour of darkness and peril and need,
The people will waken and listen to hear
The hurrying hoof-beats of that steed
And the midnight message of Paul Revere.

VICTORY

Mary Britton Miller

There was a young man
Who lived below
A mountain crowned
With glaciers and snow.

"Beautiful mountain,"
He used to say,
"Only the clouds
And the eagles know
Their way to the place
I intend to go.
The lofty peak
You lift so high
I've vowed to climb
Before I die."

When he was a man
He attempted it twice —
Bravely he scaled
Those shoulders of snow
And the arms of ice,
But for all his courage
The young man failed
In his enterprise.

Then the mountain said
In his awful voice
Of glacier and ice,
"I am here alone
With the eagles and clouds,
And forever alone
I intend to remain."
"Beautiful mountain,"
The young man replied,
"I shall try it again."

So he started out
With all the gear
That people wear
When they try to scale
A mountain's crest,
And believe it or not,
He got to the top
Of Mount Everest.

ELDORADO

Edgar Allan Poe

Gaily bedight,
    A gallant knight,
In sunshine and in shadow,
    Had journeyed long,
    Singing a song,
In search of Eldorado.

But he grew old —
This knight so bold, —
And o'er his heart a shadow
Fell as he found
No spot of ground
That looked like Eldorado.

And, as his strength
Failed him at length,
He met a pilgrim shadow.
"Shadow," said he,
"Where can it be —
This land of Eldorado?"

"Over the Mountain
Of the Moon,
Down the Valley of the Shadow,
Ride, boldly ride,"
The shade replied,
"If you seek for Eldorado!"

THE SEA GYPSY

Richard Hovey

I am fevered with the sunset,
I am fretful with the bay,
For the wander-thirst is on me
And my soul is in Cathay.

There's a schooner in the offing,
With her topsails shot with fire,
And my heart has gone aboard her
For the Islands of Desire.

I must forth again tomorrow!
With the sunset I must be,
Hull down on the trail of rapture
In the wonder of the Sea.

SPACE

Inez Hogan

When I'm big I want to be
A space cadet so I shall see
All the planets out in space —
I'll be a rocketeer, an ace.

I will fly a rocket ship
Zoom! I'll blast off on a trip
To the moon. Through space I'll fly —
In seas of space, beyond the sky.

I'll have space suits and helmets,too.
One for each man in the crew,
So we can breathe when we get there.
(Around the moon there is no air.)

When you're on the moon you weigh
Very little — so they say.
So we'll bounce around and then
We'll zoom back to earth again.

THE ARRIVAL OF THE GREENHORN

Archer Butler Hulbert

I've just got across the plains.
    I'm poorer than a snail;
My mules all died but poor old Skip.
    Who I pulled in by the tail.
I fed him last at Chimney Rock —
    That's where the grass gave out;
I'm proud to tell we stood it well
    Along the Truckee route.
But I am very weak and lean,
    Though I started plump and fat;
How I wish I had the gold machine
    I left back on the Platte.
And a pair of striped bedtick pants
    My Sally made for me
To wear while digging after gold;
    And when I left says she:
"Here, take the laudanum with you, Sam,
    To check the misiree."

THE MERRY MINER

Constance Rourke

> Go roll a prairie up like cloth,
>   Drink Mississippi dry,
> Put Allegheny in your hat,
>   A steamboat in your eye —
> And for your breakfast buffalo
>   Some five and twenty fry.
>
> Go kill the whole Comanche tribe,
>   Some day before you dine;
> Pick out to make your walking stick
>   A California pine;
> And then turn round and frown so **dark**
>   The sun won't dare to shine.
>
> Go whip a ton of grizzly bears
>   With nothing but a tan;
> And prove yourself by all these feats
>   To be a western man,
> And you can write a poem grand
>   If anybody can.

WE PUT ON THE BUFFALO

Robert P. Tristram Coffin

When the prairie schooner sailed
The green waves where the long grass bent,
They found America's great heart
Was bisons like a continent.

Out of dawn and into night
The buffalo roared endless by,
The sound of them shook all the earth,
The dust of them filled all the sky.

Proud curved necks and shaggy brows,
And little red eyes sparked with flame,
Earth's marrow, might, and loveliness
Stampeded on before the tame.

Red Indians in bisons' skins
Crept upon them, sprang, and killed,
White men's world-wide fires swept,
Ate them, and their blood was spilled.

Their bones were heavy on the land,
Their wide skulls glimmered through the night,
Yet their thunder passed into
America's marrow and our might.

Every tinker went in fur,
Each baker robed himself for snow,
Each farmer put the prairie on,
All men wore the buffalo.

All Americans put their arms,
All Americans put their thighs
In the silky wilderness
And grew tremendous in their size.

We put on the buffalo,
We put on the world and wonder,
The hot strength of the Promised Land,
We put on the sun and thunder!

CITIZENS IN THE ROUND

Robert P. Tristram Coffin

New England was tall clippers
Leaning around the globe,
New England was small pumpkins
And boys called Seth and Job.

New England was white steeples,
The white-haired hired man,
A hundred schooners blossoming out
Of the Mediterranean.

Small farms had feet in water,
The front yard curved a bit,
And Table Rock, Sumatra
Got taken into it.

New England wives made piecrust
All over the Celebes
And hung the Monday wash between
The legs of Hercules.

Farm babies teethed off Chile,
In China Sea slept sound,
They crept on decks and grew up
Citizens in the round.

They thought in tea and teakwood,
Volcanoes, longitudes,
But thought in one-horse haying,
Rhode Island hens and broods.

They never sailed so far
But church bells called them back,
Sharp crabapples to gather,
New-mown hay to stack.

And when, white-haired and quiet,
They hoed small plots of corn,
They lived by wind and weather
As once off bleak Cape Horn.

OLD LOG HOUSE

James S. Tippett

On a little green knoll
At the edge of the wood
My great great grandmother's
First house stood.

The house was of logs
My grandmother said
With one big room
And a lean-to shed.

The logs were cut
And the house was raised
By pioneer men
In the olden days.

I like to hear
My grandmother tell
How they built the fireplace
And dug the well.

They split the shingles;
They filled each chink;
It's a house of which
I like to think.

Forever and ever
I wish I could
Live in a house
At the edge of a wood.

LULLABY FOR PEREGRINE

Robert P. Tristram Coffin

Hush, new baby, bob-cats creep
Through woods three thousand dark miles deep
   Behind thy cradle, and their eyes
   Are many as the fireflies.

Hush! lean Red Men wake and prowl,
And the great, white, stealthy owl
   Shows deep eyes like burning coals,
   And the bears have left their holes.

Hush! lonely one, thou liest curled
Upon the edge of this new world,
   And all the babies that will be
   Are lying in this crib with thee.

Hush! ten million men with saws,
Hammers, axes, and new laws

Out of this small crib will creep
After thou hast done with sleep.

Hush! the woods grow dark and still
Save for the sad-voiced whippoorwill.
Sleep and rest. When thou wilt wake,
There'll be a shining world to make!

CHRISTOPHER COLUMBUS

Stephen Vincent Benét

There are lots of queer things that discoverers do
But his was the queerest, I swear.
He discovered our country in One Four Nine Two
By thinking it couldn't be there.

It wasn't his folly, it wasn't his fault,
For the very best maps of the day
Showed nothing but water, extensive and salt,
On the West, between Spain and Bombay.

There were monsters, of course, every watery mile,
Great krakens with blubbery lips
And sea-serpents smiling a crocodile-smile
As they waited for poor little ships.

There were whirlpools and maelstroms, without any doubt
And tornadoes of lava and ink.
(Which, as nobody yet had been there to find out,
Seems a little bit odd, don't you think?)

But Columbus was bold and Columbus set sail
(Thanks to Queen Isabella, her pelf),
For he said "Though there may be both monster and gale,
I'd like to find out for myself."

And he sailed and he sailed and he *sailed* and he SAILED,
Though his crew would have gladly turned round
And, morning and evening, distressfully wailed
"This is running things into the ground!"

But he paid no attention to protest or squall,
This obstinate son of the mast,
And so, in the end, he discovered us all,
Remarking, "Here's India, at last!"

He didn't intend it, he meant to heave to
At Calcutta, Rangoon or Shanghai,
There are many queer things that discoverers do,
But his was the queerest. Oh my!

LEWIS AND CLARK

Stephen Vincent Benét

Lewis and Clark
Said, "Come on, let's embark
For a boating trip up the Missouri!
It's the President's wish
And we might catch some fish,
Though the river is muddy as fury."

So they started away
On a breezy May day,
Full of courage and lore scientific,
And, before they came back,
They had blazed out a track
From St. Louis straight to the Pacific.

Now, if *you* want to go
From St. Louis (in Mo.)
To Portland (the Ore. not the Me. one),
You can fly there in planes
Or board limited trains
Or the family car, if there be one.

It may take you two weeks,
If your car's full of squeaks
And you stop for the sights and the strangers,
But it took them (don't laugh!)

Just one year and a half,
Full of buffalo, Indians and dangers.

They ate prairie-dog soup
When they suffered from croup,
For the weather was often quite drizzly.
They learned "How do you do?"
In Shoshone and Sioux,
And how to be chased by a grizzly.

They crossed mountain and river
With never a quiver,
And the Rockies themselves weren't too big for them,
For they scrambled across
With their teeth full of moss,
But their fiddler still playing a jig for them.

Missouri's Great Falls,
And the Yellowstone's walls
And the mighty Columbia's billows,
They viewed or traversed,
Of all white men the first
To make the whole Northwest their pillows.

And, when they returned,
It was glory well-earned
That they gave to the national chorus,
They were ragged and lean
But they'd seen what they'd seen
And it spread out an Empire before us.

CLIPPER SHIPS AND CAPTAINS

Stephen Vincent Benét

There was a time before our time,
It will not come again,
When the best ships still were wooden ships
But the men were iron men.

From Stonington to Kennebunk
The Yankee hammers plied
To build the clippers of the wave
That were New England's pride.

The "Flying Cloud," the "Northern Light,"
The "Sovereign of the Seas"
— There was salt music in the blood
That thought of names like these.

"Sea Witch," "Red Jacket," "Golden Age"
And "Chariot of Fame,"
The whole world gaped to look at them
Before the steamship came.

Their cargoes were of tea and gold,
Their bows a cutting blade,
And, on the poop, the skippers walked,
Lords of the China trade.

The skippers with the little beards
And the New England drawl
Who knew Hong Kong and Marblehead
And the Pole Star over all.

Stately as churches, swift as gulls,
They trod the oceans, then —
No man had seen such ships before
And none will see again.

MISSOURI RHAPSODY

James Daugherty

The dim script on the yellow sheets of pioneer diaries,
the old journals, the faded letters, call up pictures
of the slow processions, the lumbering white-tops, the plod-
    ding caravans
moving across the rolling prairie toward the white peaks.

Out of the crowded lines of the brown script rises a kind of
    music.
The creak of wagon wheels, the lowing of tired cattle, and
    the harsh song of mules.
The whinnying of horses and the ring of the blacksmith's
    anvil.

There is the rank smell of sweat and harness and the sweet
   odor of cook fires.

The quick plucking of banjos and guitars,
the thud of booted feet dancing to "Turkey in the Straw."
The refrain of the old hymns of faith, "Rock of Ages, Truth
   divine,"
and the gray wolf's cry of desolation across the dark.
The driven rain beating on the dirt roof of prairie soddies
and the canvas tent of the immigrant.

The rhythms of galloping hoofs and the thunder of the buffalo herd,
the bark of rifle fire repelling the Indian surprise,
the screams of women and the groaned prayers of the hurt
   and dying.
Crescendo and diminuendo, the voices speaking out of the
   yellow diaries.

The music of the western trails rises out of the pages of the
   pioneer journals,
the letters scrawled by the campfires, in the canyons and
   mountain passes along the old western trails.

GATES OF THE ROCKIES

James Daugherty

Down the carved hills the bison come
To the cool wet buffalo wallows.
The monstrous bulls with dripping mane
Splash through the river shallows.
In the bottomlands the elk herd stands
And crops the flower-strewn grass.
By rushes rank along the bank
White swans swim slowly past.

WHEEL RUTS

James Daugherty

Old wheel ruts deep still mark the trace
Where the prairie schooners passed this place.
A name marked faint on a crumbling stone,
In the desert dust a whitened bone,
Bleached bone in the desert dust
And iron wheel-rim red with rust.
The form forgotten but still we find
The living image of the mind.
In cloud shapes in the wind-swept sky
The long processions still roll by,
Still drifting high above Pike's Peak
Across the blue and white tips streak.

301

TRAIL BREAKERS

James Daugherty

I

We remember, we do not forget, O Trail Breakers.
Mountain Men, Missourians, following the rivers,
Platte, Yellowstone, Sweetwater, Columbia;
Crossing the Great Divide, the mountain passes,
The dusty cavalcades are coming over the mountains —
The Big Horns, the Wind, the Tetons, the Medicine Bow,
The Bitterroot, the Sierras, the Cascades,
The wind in the Great South Pass remembers the lost
trappers.

II

Under the red bluffs plod the slow wagon trains, the white-
tops,
Come the dusty processions along the Oregon Trail and the
Santa Fe, the lumbering prairie schooners,
Bringing the prairie breakers, the plowmen, the pioneer
women, bringing the bull-tongue plows
To break the tough sod, in the Dakotas, Nebraska,
Ioway, Minnesota, sowing the corn, the wheat, the golden
seas.
The pioneer mothers in the sod huts, to breed strong sons
And tall daughters in the sod huts of the Kansas prairie.
To make statebuilders of the West, Montana, Wyoming,
Washington,

To frame the western democracies, Utah, Colorado, Idaho,
Nevada, Oregon.

III

Pack train, stage coach, pony express, climb over the moun-
tain passes;
The Iron Horse roars west, spouting smoke and cinders,
The continental express streaks on, faster, faster, faster.
On the six-lane highways the sleek speedsters are streaming
west;
The airliner drones across the sky, six hours from coast to
coast.
The jet plane, the supersonic rocket, trail a white line across
the blue.
The mushroom blast of the H bomb announces
the terror and the splendor of the
Atomic Age.

I MAY, I MIGHT, I MUST

Marianne Moore

> If you will tell me why the fen
> appears impassable, I then
> will tell you why I think that I
> can get across it if I try.

IF I WERE A PILGRIM CHILD

Rowena Bennett

If I were a Pilgrim child,
   Dressed in white or gray,
I should catch my turkey wild
   For Thanksgiving Day.
I should pick my cranberries
   Fresh from out a bog,
And make a table of a stump
   And sit upon a log.
An Indian would be my guest
   And wear a crimson feather,
And we should clasp our hands and say
   Thanksgiving grace together.
But I was born in modern times
   And shall not have this joy.
My cranberries will be delivered
   By the grocery boy.
My turkey will be served upon
   A shining silver platter.
It will not taste as wild game tastes
   Though it will be much fatter;
And, oh, of all the guests that come
   Not one of them will wear
   Moccasins upon his feet
   Or feathers in his hair!

INDIAN NAMES

Lydia Huntly Sigourney

Ye say they all have passed away,
   That noble race and brave;
That their light canoes have vanished
   From off the crested wave;
That mid the forests where they roamed,
   There rings no hunter's shout:
But their name is on your waters,
   Ye may not wash it out.

'Tis where Ontario's billow
   Like Ocean's surge is curled,
Where strong Niagara's thunders wake
   The echo of the world;
Where red Missouri bringeth
   Rich tribute from the west;
And Rappahannock sweetly sleeps
   On green Virginia's breast.

Ye say their conelike cabins,
   That clustered o'er the vale,
Have disappeared as withered leaves
   Before the autumn gale:
But their memory liveth on your hills,
   Their baptism on your shore,
Your everlasting rivers speak
   Their dialect of yore.

Old Massachusetts wears it
  Within her lordly crown,
And broad Ohio bears it
  Amid his young renown;
Connecticut hath wreathed it
  Where her quiet foliage waves.
And bold Kentucky breathes it hoarse
  Through all her ancient caves.

Wachusett hides its lingering voice
  Within its rocky heart,
And Allegheny graves its tone
  Throughout his lofty chart.
Monadnock, on his forehead hoar,
  Doth seal the sacred trust:
Your mountains build their monument,
  Though ye destroy their dust.

THE CLOSING OF THE RODEO

William Jay Smith

The lariat snaps; the cowboy rolls
  His pack, and mounts and rides away.
Back to the land the cowboy goes.

Plumes of smoke from the factory sway
  In the setting sun. The curtain falls,
A train in the darkness pulls away.

Good-by, says the rain on the iron roofs.
  Good-by, say the barber poles.
Dark drum the vanishing horses' hooves.

THE KAYAK

Unknown

Over the briny wave I go,
In spite of the weather, in spite of the snow:
What cares the hardy Eskimo?
In my little skiff, with paddle and lance,
I glide where the foaming billows dance.

Round me the sea-birds slip and soar;
Like me, they love the ocean's roar.
Sometimes a floating iceberg gleams
Above me with its melting streams;
Sometimes a rushing wave will fall
Down on my skiff and cover it all.

But what care I for a wave's attack?
With my paddle I right my little kayak,
And then its weight I speedily trim,
And over the water away I skim.

THE CAPTAINS OF SMALL FARMS

Robert P. Tristram Coffin

Yankee captains and their wives
Rounding the Winter Horn
Thought of snowing apple bloom
And the sprouting corn.

They could not get seasons of home
Out of their bright brains,
They heard the sleigh bells tingling through
The yellow Monsoon rains.

Among ghosts of Antarctic ice
They thought of cutting hay —
"I wonder now how many loads
Old Dick hauled in today?"

White Cadiz, red Trieste loomed high,
Strange melons shone like gold —
"Today the pumpkins will be cut
And the house banked for the cold."

In storms of pigeons and wild bells
By Lions of St. Mark —
"I hope they think to take the calf
In before it's dark."

"Why, bless me! it's fairtime again
Home now, I declare!"
And the blood-red Pyrenees
Towered in the air.

Lands full of lost great loveliness,
Haunted by nymphs and Pan —
"We must be home in time to taste
New cider if we can."

Along walls of a burnt-out world,
Hercules waded the sea —
"I wonder, is the popcorn sweet
As it used to be?"

MY FATHER LOVED THE JUMPING-OFF PLACE

Robert P. Tristram Coffin

My Father was a pioneer,
A very handsome man,
When he laid his codfish in,
He laid in for a clan.

He salted herring by the ton,
He bought in hogsheads, tierces,
He turned his host of boys and girls
Out in the weather's mercies.

He wanted them to be good friends
With twelve winds and weather.
The house he ran up had hard time
Keeping them all together.

He built it on the jumping-off
Island far out at sea,
He had to chain it down each night
To know where it would be.

And when the wind changed, he would have
To rise in his night-tails
And shift the ox-chains over it
To suit the midnight gales.

The beets had to be anchored down,
And our White Leghorns tethered,
We grew up a handsome lot,
Beautifully weathered.

The cow we had — I guess for me —
Went to the landward shore
And lowed her soul towards the main
And cows she knew of yore.

The days went by lonely as loons,
I learned to creep on ledges,
I went to sleep by lighthouses
On the world's blue edges.

I rowed a boat before I walked,
I caught rock-cod before
I knew the alphabet, the whole
Atlantic filled my door.

Sometimes I think that windblown place
Made me what I am,
Sometimes I think my father was
Noah or Abraham.

ABRAHAM LINCOLN WALKS AT MIDNIGHT
(In Springfield, Illinois)

Vachel Lindsay

It is portentous, and a thing of state
    That here at midnight, in our little town
A mourning figure walks, and will not rest,
    Near the old court-house pacing up and down.

Or by his homestead, or in shadowed yards
    He lingers where his children used to play,
Or through the market, on the well-worn stones
    He stalks until the dawn-stars burn away.

A bronzed, lank man! His suit of ancient black,
    A famous high top-hat and plain worn shawl
Make him the quaint great figure that the men love,
    The prairie lawyer, master of us all.

He cannot sleep upon his hillside now.
  He is among us: — as in times before!
And we who toss and lie awake for long
  Breathe deep, and start, to see him pass the door.

His head is bowed. He thinks on men and kings.
  Yea, when the sick world cries, how can he sleep?
Too many peasants fight, they know not why,
  Too many homesteads in black terror weep.

The sins of all the war-lords burn his heart.
  He sees the dreadnoughts scouring every main.
He carries on his shawl-wrapped shoulders now
  The bitterness, the folly and the pain.

CAVALRY CROSSING A FORD

Walt Whitman

A line in long array where they wind betwixt green islands,
They take a serpentine course, their arms flash in the sun —
  hark to the musical clank,
Behold the silvery river, in it the splashing horses loitering
  stop to drink,
Behold the brown-faced men, each group, each person a
  picture, the negligent rest on the saddles,
Some emerge on the opposite bank, others are just entering
  the ford — while,
Scarlet and blue and snowy white,
The guidon flags flutter gayly in the wind.

GRANDMOTHER'S VISIT

William Wise

This morning I was bad,
But it really didn't matter:
I came down the stairs
With a terrible clatter;
I jumped and I shouted,
I tried to pinch sister,
I called father "Pop"
and the garbage man "Mister";
I pretended I was deaf
And I said I liked beer.
But it really won't matter
'Cause Grandmother's here.

When Grandmother's here,
Then everything's fine:
She says a boy shouts
To strengthen his spine;
She says a boy jumps
To make him grow tall;
And when I pretend
She doesn't mind at all.
This morning I was bad,
But there's nothing to fear;
My troubles are over
When Grandmother's here!

NANCY HANKS

Rosemary Carr Benét

If Nancy Hanks
Came back as a ghost,
Seeking news
Of what she loved most,
She'd ask first
"Where's my son?
What's happened to Abe?
What's he done?

"Poor little Abe,
Left all alone
Except for Tom,
Who's a rolling stone;
He was only nine
The year I died.
I remember still
How hard he cried.

"Scraping along
In a little shack,
With hardly a shirt
To cover his back,
And a prairie wind
To blow him down,
Or pinching times
If he went to town.

"You wouldn't know
About my son?
Did he grow tall?
Did he have fun?
Did he learn to read?
Did he get to town?
Do you know his name?
Did he get on?"

A MORTIFYING MISTAKE

Anna Maria Pratt

I studied my tables over and over, and backward and forward, too;
But I couldn't remember six times nine, and I didn't know
what to do,
'Til sister told me to play with my doll, and not to bother my
head.
"If you call her 'Fifty-four' for a while, you'll learn it by
heart," she said.

So I took my favorite, Mary Ann (though I thought 'twas a
dreadful shame
To give such a perfectly lovely child such a perfectly horrible
name),
And I called her my dear little 'Fifty-four' a hundred times,
till I knew
The answer of six times nine as well as the answer of two
times two.

Next day Elizabeth Wigglesworth, who always acts so proud,
Said "Six times nine is fifty-two," and I nearly laughed
aloud!
But I wished I hadn't when teacher said, "Now, Dorothy, tell
if you can."
For I thought of my doll and — sakes alive! — I answered,
"Mary Ann!"

ANTIQUE SHOP

Carl Carmer

I knew an old lady
A long time ago
Who rocked while she told me
The things I should know.

She lies in her grave now
And I am a man
But here is her rocker
And here is her fan.

Her fan and her rocker
Are all that remain
But I can still see her
Rock-rocking,
Talk-talking,
Rock-rocking
Again.

GRACE ANANNE

Lysbeth Boyd Borie

The little girls that live next door
Both are twins and both are four

And I try hard but never can
Tell which is Grace and which is Anne.

Now if I ever need just Grace
To help me build a cooking place

Or if I ever need just Anne
To help play "I'm the Doctor Man"

The only thing that I can do
When I need one is yell for two,

And that is how it all began
About my yelling — "Grace AnAnne!"

Animal
Poems

THE LION AND THE MOUSE

Jeffreys Taylor

A lion with the heat oppressed,
One day composed himself to rest:
But while he dozed as he intended,
A mouse, his royal back ascended;
Nor thought of harm, as Aesop tells,
Mistaking him for someone else;
And travelled over him, and round him,
And might have left him as she found him
Had she not — tremble when you hear —
Tried to explore the monarch's ear!
Who straightway woke, with wrath immense,
And shook his head to cast her thence.
"You rascal, what are you about,"
Said he, when he had turned her out,
"I'll teach you soon," the lion said,
"To make a mouse-hole in my head!"
So saying, he prepared his foot
To crush the trembling tiny brute;
But she (the mouse) with tearful eye,
Implored the lion's clemency,
Who thought it best at last to give
His little prisoner a reprieve.

'Twas nearly twelve months after this,
The lion chanced his way to miss;
When pressing forward, heedless yet,

He got entangled in a net.
With dreadful rage, he stamped and tore,
And straight commenced a lordly roar;
When the poor mouse, who heard the noise,
Attended, for she knew his voice.
Then what the lion's utmost strength
Could not effect, she did at length;
With patient labor she applied
Her teeth, the network to divide;
And so at last forth issued he,
A *lion*, by a mouse set free.

Few are so small or weak, I guess,
But may assist us in distress,
Nor shall we ever, if we're wise,
The meanest, or the least despise.

MACAVITY: THE MYSTERY CAT

T. S. Eliot

Macavity's a Mystery Cat: he's called the Hidden Paw —
For he's the master criminal who can defy the Law.
He's the bafflement of Scotland Yard, the Flying Squad's
    despair:
For when they reach the scene of crime — MACAVITY'S
    NOT THERE!

Macavity, Macavity, there's no one like Macavity,
He's broken every human law, he breaks the law of gravity.
His powers of levitation would make a fakir stare,
And when you reach the scene of crime — MACAVITY'S
NOT THERE!

Macavity's a ginger cat, he's very tall and thin;
You would know him if you saw him, for his eyes are sunken
in.
His brow is deeply lined with thought, his head is highly
domed;
His coat is dusty from neglect, his whiskers are uncombed.
He sways his head from side to side, with movements like a
snake;
And when you think he's half-asleep, he's always wide
awake.

Macavity, Macavity, there's no one like Macavity,
For he's a fiend in feline shape, a monster of depravity.
You may meet him in a by-street, you may see him in the
square —
But when a crime's discovered, then MACAVITY'S NOT
THERE!

He's outwardly respectable. (They say he cheats at cards.)
And his footprints are not found in any file of Scotland
Yard's.
And when the larder's looted, or the jewel-case is rifled,
Or when the milk is missing, or another Peke's been stifled,

Or the greenhouse glass is broken, and the trellis past re-
   pair —
Ay, there's the wonder of the thing! MACAVITY'S NOT
   THERE!

And when the Foreign Office find a Treaty's gone astray,
Or the Admiralty lose some plans and drawings by the way,
There may be a scrap of paper in the hall or on the stair —
But it's useless to investigate — MACAVITY'S NOT
   THERE!
And when the loss has been disclosed, the Secret Service say:
"It *must* have been Macavity!" but he's a mile away.
You'll be sure to find him resting, or a-licking of his thumbs,
Or engaged in doing complicated long division sums.

Macavity, Macavity, there's no one like Macavity,
There never was a Cat of such deceitfulness and suavity.
He always has an alibi, and one or two to spare:
At whatever time the deed took place — MACAVITY
   WASN'T THERE!
And they say that all the Cats whose wicked deeds are widely
   known
(I might mention Mungojerrie, I might mention Griddlebone)
Are nothing more than agents for the Cat who all the time
Just controls their operations: the Napoleon of Crime!

THE NAMING OF CATS

T. S. Eliot

The Naming of Cats is a difficult matter,
    It isn't just one of your holiday games;
You may think at first I'm as mad as a hatter
      When I tell you, a cat must have THREE DIFFERENT
      NAMES,
First of all, there's the name that the family use daily,
    Such as Peter, Augustus, Alonzo or James,
Such as Victor or Jonathan, George or Bill Bailey —
    All of them sensible everyday names.
There are fancier names if you think they sound sweeter,
    Some for the gentlemen, some for the dames:
Such as Plato, Admetus, Electra, Demeter —
    But all of them sensible everyday names.
But I tell you, a cat needs a name that's particular,
    A name that's peculiar, and more dignified,
Else how can he keep up his tail perpendicular,
    Or spread out his whiskers, or cherish his pride?
Of names of this kind, I can give you a quorum,
    Such as Munkustrap, Quaxo, or Coricopat,
Such as Bombalurina, or else Jellylorum —
    Names that never belong to more than one cat.
But above and beyond there's still one name left over,
    And that is the name that you never will guess;
The name that no human research can discover —
      But THE CAT HIMSELF KNOWS, and will never con-
      fess.

When you notice a cat in profound meditation,
    The reason, I tell you, is always the same:
His mind is engaged in a rapt contemplation
    Of the thought, of the thought, of the thought of his name:
        His ineffable effable
        Effanineffable
Deep and inscrutable singular Name.

THE SNAIL

James Reeves

At sunset, when the night-dews fall,
Out of the ivy on the wall
With horns outstretched and pointed tail
Comes the grey and noiseless snail.
On ivy stems she clambers down,
Carrying her house of brown.
Safe in the dark, no greedy eye
Can her tender body spy,
While she herself, a hungry thief,
Searches out the freshest leaf.
She travels on as best she can
Like a toppling caravan.

DOG IN A CAR

David McCord

He grins a little as they drive him by.
Of what his nose needs there's a fresh supply
Round every corner, up the rainy field,
He has no daily walk of equal yield.
His head hangs out, his tongue out farther still;
His bark is bolder from that window sill,
His nose is longer on the modern breeze —
His father being Scotch, not Pekingese.

A lesser breed on leash or running loose
Would find his comradeship of little use;
A dog transported by the family Ford
Rides far beyond the days he loved or warred.
His ancestors on purely urban smells
Leaned hard enough, but they had nothing else.
They hadn't won to his synthetic taste:
Investigation kept them out of haste.

You drive a dog from State to other State:
His senses meet with scents he can't relate.
He hasn't time. His little nostrils twitch.
Was that a rabbit, mole, or brindle bitch?
His eyes grow bright. He reaches out in space.
The local brothers hardly see his face.
He's whirling through a night of strange impact:
Of atavistic cats he once attacked.

HEN OVERBOARD

Robert P. Tristram Coffin

"All hands alive! We're goin' about!"
Old Captain Cobb was white as chalk,
He spun the wheel in his wide hands,
"I've lost Sal's best Barred Plymouth Rock!"

The vast white bellied sails went flat,
A thousand ropes began to whine,
Round-eyed sailors gripped the yards,
"I'll catch it from that wife of mine!"

"Sal took her off her setting-eggs
To sun her on the after-hatch.
The breezes caught her. Man the boat!
Or I know what I'm going to catch!"

Under Java's sky-high peaks,
In the strait of Sunda's foam,
The prim New England biddy-hen
Screamed for help and squalled for home.

She knew this was a godless place,
She saw the wicked sperm whales play
And fish that flew, and knew home was
Twelve thousand watery miles away.

The mighty Yankee ship came round,
The davits squealed, down went the boat,
Away it rowed, and Captain Cobb
Found Plymouth Rock was still afloat.

He tucked her in his best frock coat
He soothed her woes as best he could,
Home he brought her to her eggs,
New England, God, and motherhood.

FISH

William Jay Smith

Look at the fish!
Look at the fish!

Look at the fish that is blue and green,
Look at the fish that is tangerine!
Look at the fish that is gold and black
With monocled eye and big humpback!
Look at the fish with the ring in his nose,
And a mouth he cannot open or close!
Look at the fish with lavender stripes
And long front teeth like organ pipes,
And fins that are finer than Irish lace.
Look at that funny grin on his face,
Look at him swimming all over the place!

328

Look at the fish!
Look at the fish!
Look at the fish!
They're so beautiful.

THE PROUD TOAD

Grace Taber Hallock

I often see a puffy toad
Squatting proudly in the road.
He never sees a passer-by
Unless it is a juicy fly.

GRASSHOPPER HOP-O-THE GRASSES

Grace Taber Hallock

Grasshopper, grasshopper, hop-o-the grasses,
I caught you because you can give me molasses.
Grasshopper, give some molasses to me,
And grasshopper, grasshopper, you shall go free.

MUD TURTLES

Grace Taber Hallock

On the rock the turtles get
When they are tired of being wet.
Back into the pond they slide
When they are tired of being dried.

THE DOG AND THE CAT

Grace Taber Hallock

In the house I have a cat
To cuddle up and feed and pat,
But out of doors, where I am free,
I have a dog to follow me.

IN THE BARNYARD

Dorothy Aldis

In the barnyard chickens walk, —
They jerk their heads and pick and talk,

While yellow ducklings run around
Like butter balls upon the ground,
And some geese, tremendous proud,
Point their noses at a cloud.

THE PLEASANT COW

Grace Taber Hallock

The moo cow is a mammal NOT
As haughty as a camel, NOR
As naughty as a cannibal,
But just a pleasant animal.

SNAKES AND SNAILS

Grace Taber Hallock

Through the grasses tall and slim
All about the water's rim,
Lie the slimy secret trails
Of the water-snakes and snails.

WHO'S THERE?

Frances Frost

Somebody knocked
In the windless wood,
Insistent and loud.
Startled, I stood
Among steep pines
And looked around.
There was nothing
But snowy ground
And drifted tracks
Where deer had been.
Did somebody want
To get out or in?

Somebody knocked
Again and again.
I looked up
At the old birch then.
Three-toed he clung
Like a quizzical clown,
Gazing at me
Upside down —
A woodpecker trying
Not to grow thin,
Who wanted neither
Out nor in!

CLOVER FOR BREAKFAST

Frances Frost

Upon the sunny summer hill,
As I was lying in the grass,
I caught my breath, I held my breath,
To see a mother woodchuck pass.

Behind her trotted four young chucks
On anxious and unsteady feet:
When she halted in a clover patch,
You should have seen them eat!

You should have seen them sitting up
With clover blossoms in their paws:
Their infant eyes were bright. I smiled
To see their small and busy jaws!

Oh, red and white and purple bloom —
That was a fragrant morning feast!
Motionless I lay and watched
And didn't scare them in the least.

Then Happily the mother led
Her small brown babies home anew;
And I think, in the green and shady wood,
She tucked them in — don't you?

SQUIRREL IN THE RAIN

Frances Frost

The young squirrel's mother said, "Come out!"
See — it's raining all about!
Wet silver's falling from a cloud!
It's raining hard, it's raining loud!"

The little squirrel ran down the tree:
"It's splashing rain all over me!
It's raining here, it's raining there!
It's raining in trees' green hair,
It's raining in the flowers' faces,
It's raining in the grassy places,
It's raining on my tail and nose
And on my middle, I suppose!
How wonderful of clouds to fly
And give young squirrels a drink of sky!"

TAILS

Rowena Bennett

The kangaroo has a heavy tail
She sits on for a chair.

There's scarcely any tail at all
   Upon the polar bear.
But the monkey has the nicest tail
   Of any living thing,
For he can hook it to a branch
   And use it as a swing.

SQUIRREL

James S. Tippett

Mrs. Squirrel
   In a tree
Arched her tail
   And scolded me.

"Those nuts are mine,"
   She seemed to say.
"Leave them for me;
   Go 'way, go 'way!"

She jerked her tail;
   She bobbed her head.
I will not tell you
   ALL she said.

QUESTIONS FOR A
FLYING SQUIRREL TO ANSWER

Rachel Field

Who are you that can fly,
Or hide in a crumpled leaf;
To whom my hand is a vast
Pink plain of space and wonder?
Who breathed on your sleek, gray coat
That it should be thistledown soft,
And thicker than velvet mullein?
How were your whiskers spun,
More fine than silver thread?
Why are your claws so frail,
Like frost, with as eerie a coldness?
How came your tail to be
Flat as dove's breast-feather?
Who taught you to fold it close
In a curl about your haunches?
Why are your eyes so black,
So restless and ever shining
Under your pointed ears?
And how can a small heart beat
So fast in a tiny body?

CRADLE SONG OF THE ELEPHANTS

Adriano del Valle
Trans. by Alida Malkus

The little elephant was crying
because it did not want to sleep . . .
Go to sleep, my little elephant,
the moon is going to hear you weep.

Papa elephant is near.
I hear him bellowing among the mangoes.
Go to sleep, my little elephant,
the moon will hear my little fellow . . .

BUTTERFLY

William Jay Smith

Of living creatures most I prize
Black-spotted yellow Butterflies
Sailing softly through the skies,

Whisking light from each sunbeam,
Gliding over field and stream —
Like fans unfolding in a dream,

Like fans of gold lace flickering
Before a drowsy elfin king
For whom the thrush and linnet sing —

Soft and beautiful and bright
As hands that move to touch the light
When Mother leans to say good night.

ONCE I NEARLY TOUCHED A BIRD

Mary Jane Carr

Once I nearly touched a bird —
    I nearly touched it with my hand;
It let me come so close, so close,
    And seemed to understand.

I really didn't want to catch it —
    Just to touch its feathers gray —
But something made a noise and scared it,
    And it flew away.

So close, so close it let me come;
    He stood and never even stirred;
In all my life I hadn't been
    So close up to a bird!

I could see its black eyes glisten;
   "Why, hello!" they seemed to say;
But something made a noise and scared it,
   And it flew away.

BLUE ON WHITE

Elizabeth Coatsworth

This clearing day
Of white and blue
Called for some life
To make it true.

Something moving
Across the snow,
Something across
Such sky to go.

No sooner had I
Finished thinking
Than a shadow appeared
As quick as winking.

And looking up
To the apple tree's gray
I saw in bare boughs
A proud blue jay.

His head was crested,
His tail was long,
His color was bright,
His beak was strong.

Boldly and calmly
He looked forth
Over sun and snow
And then flew north!

THE BLACKBIRD

Humbert Wolfe

In the far corner,
close by the swings,
every morning
a blackbird sings.

His bill's so yellow,
his coat's so black,
that he makes a fellow
whistle back.

Ann, my daughter,
thinks that he
sings for us two
especially.

WILD GEESE

Elinor Chipp

I heard the wild geese flying
  In the dead of the night,
With beat of wings and crying
I heard the wild geese flying,
And dreams in my heart sighing
  Followed their northward flight.
I heard the wild geese flying
  In the dead of the night.

CHARM FOR GOING A-HUNTING

Mary Austin

O my brothers of the wilderness,
My little brothers,
For my necessities I am about to kill you!
May the Master of Life who made you
In the form of the quarry
That my children may be fed,
Speedily provide you another house;
So there may be peace
Between me and thy spirit.

341

YOUNG FLASH THE DEER

Thornton Burgess

His eyes are big and soft and bright;
His lifted tail is snowy white;

He's light of foot and where he goes
He leaves the prints of pointed toes.

With pride he holds his antlered head
Until, alas, his crown is shed.

Over fence and fallen trees
He lightly bounds with graceful ease.

YAK

William Jay Smith

The long-haired Yak has long black hair,
He lets it grow — he doesn't care.
He lets it grow and grow and grow,
He lets it trail along the stair.
Does he ever go to the barbershop? NO!
How wild and woolly and devil-may-care
A long-haired Yak with long black hair
Would look when perched in a barber chair!

PADDY THE BEAVER

Thornton Burgess

Although a lumberman 'tis clear
The Beaver is an engineer.

He digs canals, the clever chap,
And builds a dam without a gap
Across a stream to make a pond,
Then builds his house out just beyond.

To signal danger without fail
He slaps the water with his tail.

THE RUNAWAY

Robert Frost

Once, when the snow of the year was beginning to fall,
We stopped by a mountain pasture to say "Whose colt?"
A little Morgan had one forefoot on the wall,
The other curled at his breast. He dipped his head
And snorted at us. And then he had to bolt.
We heard the miniature thunder where he fled
And we saw him, or thought we saw him, dim and grey,

Like a shadow against the curtain of falling flakes.
"I think the little fellow's afraid of the snow.
He isn't winter-broken. It isn't play
With the little fellow at all. He's running away.
I doubt if even his mother could tell him, 'Sakes,
It's only weather.' He'd think she didn't know!
Where is his mother? He can't be out alone."
And now he comes again with a clatter of stone,
And mounts the wall again with whited eyes
And all his tail that isn't hair up straight.
He shudders his coat as if to throw off flies.
"Whoever it is that leaves him out so late,
When other creatures have gone to stall and bin,
Ought to be told to come and take him in."

WHY NOBODY PETS THE LION AT THE ZOO

John Ciardi

The morning that the world began
The Lion growled a growl at Man.

And I suspect the Lion might
(If he'd been closer) have tried a bite.

I think that's as it ought to be
And not as it was taught to me.

344

I think the Lion has a right
To growl a growl and bite a bite.

And if the Lion bothered Adam,
He should have growled right back at 'im.

The way to treat a Lion right
Is growl for growl and bite for bite.

True, the Lion is better fit
For biting than for being bit.

But if you look him in the eye
You'll find the Lion's rather shy.

He really wants someone to pet him.
The trouble is: his teeth won't let him.

He has a heart of gold beneath
But the Lion just can't trust his teeth.

Index of Titles

351

354

Index of Authors

359

362

364

Index of First Lines

366

367

373